Satellite Environment Handbook

Satellite Environment Handbook

Edited by **Francis S. Johnson**

LOCKHEED AIRCRAFT CORPORATION

MISSILES AND SPACE DIVISION

PALO ALTO, CALIFORNIA

Stanford University Press

STANFORD, CALIFORNIA   1961

Stanford University Press
Stanford, California

Library of Congress Catalog Card Number: 61-12393

Printed in the United States of America

Preface

Data on the elements of the satellite environment are being acquired at a rapid rate, but large gaps in our knowledge of this area still exist and will continue to exist for several years at least. Knowledge in this field is growing so rapidly that we might describe it as an exploding field. Many of the phenomena described in this book were not known or even suspected three years ago. Some of our present ideas will undoubtedly have to be altered in varying degrees within the next year or two. It is probable that there are still some major surprises in store for us.

In such a situation, where our ideas concerning the space environment are developing and changing rapidly, it may appear unwise to attempt to publish a compilation of the existing data. However, there is an urgent need for the best estimates that can be made of the nature of the space environment. These estimates are particularly needed in connection with engineering projects for space systems, but such data are also required in the rapidly developing field of space physics.

The satellite-environment data presented here have been compiled principally in response to numerous questions from engineering projects directed to the Space Physics Research organization at Lockheed Missiles and Space Division. It was also recognized, however, that many research activities should also profit from the organization of data in the several fields of endeavor. Consequently, it is hoped that the data and analyses presented here will be useful in diverse research and engineering programs in space-systems development, in geophysics, in meteorology, and in other disciplines.

The available data describing the geophysical environment encountered by artificial Earth satellites are presented in a comprehensive summary. The major satellite-environment factors—the structure of the upper atmosphere and the ionosphere, penetrating-particle radiation, solar radiation, micrometeorites, radio noise, thermal radiation from Earth, and geomagnetism—are discussed, and existing data are evaluated. An effort has been made to describe these factors completely, even from insufficient experimental data, provided there is a physical basis for extrapolating from whatever data are available. Needless to say, many of the data included will require modification as more measurements are obtained.

We are indebted to our colleagues in the scientific community for many helpful and stimulating discussions on matters relating to the material presented in the book. We are grateful for the use of several figures which have been made available to us by various research groups. Working with the competent staff of the Stanford University Press has been a pleasant and informative experience. It is also a pleasure to acknowledge the assistance of Research Technical Publications at LMSD and in particular José Villarreal, who assisted in the preparation of the technical report upon which this book is based.

FRANCIS S. JOHNSON

Palo Alto, California
March 1961

ERRATA

Page 21 Table 1–2, ρ should read 7.2×10^{-19} instead of 1.38×10^{-19} g/cm³ at 900 km.

ρ should read 2.7×10^{-19} instead of 3.7×10^{-19} g/cm³ at 1000 km.

Page 50 Eleventh and twelfth lines should read $v_{\perp}$ instead of v.

Page 58 Caption of Fig. 3–4, fourth line should read Fig. 3–5a instead of Fig. 3–5b.

Page 70 Second line under Flux (for auroral protons) should read E >100 kev instead of 100 Mev.

Page 80 Table 4–2, The mean solar spectral irradiance at 1600 A should read 1.8×10^{-9} instead of 7.8×10^{-10} w/cm²-A.

Satellite Environment Handbook; Francis S. Johnson, ed.; Stanford University Press, 1961.

Contents

Tables

Illustrations

Satellite Environment Handbook

Introduction

Experimental data on the satellite environment are fairly complete in some areas (*e.g.*, solar radiation) and very fragmentary in others (*e.g.*, Van Allen radiation). Theoretical concepts can be used in varying degrees to supplement or extend the experimental data. Consequently, the degree of confidence in different elements of the satellite environment varies widely. The situation is also changing rapidly. Two years ago it would not have been possible to develop nearly so comprehensive a picture of the satellite environment as is presented here. By the same token, we can anticipate that a much more definitive and complete picture will be possible a year or two hence.

Data on the structure of the upper atmosphere fall mainly in two categories—the vertical-density profile and the composition. Satellite-orbital-decay data have vastly improved our knowledge of the density profile, especially at the higher levels, but considerable areas of uncertainty still surround the latitudinal, diurnal, and other variations which may be present. Limited composition data are available from mass-spectrometer measurements made in rockets, principally at altitudes below 220 km. With the available data, one cannot adequately describe the structure of the upper atmosphere except by introducing a number of theoretical concepts, such as those of diffusive equilibrium and conductivity control of the temperature profile. The concept of atmospheric static structure is now well developed; the over-all picture of the atmosphere seems to be complete, although refinements of our knowledge of the values of the parameters will be improved with the results of future measurements and experiments. The conceptual problems which still confront us are those relating to the dynamics of the upper atmosphere, in particular the strong wind shears.

Ionospheric data consist mainly of ground measurements made by reflecting radio signals from the ionosphere; in this way, the structure of the ionosphere up to the level of maximum electron concentration has been extensively studied for many years. A few data above the level of maximum electron concentration have recently become available, principally through measurements obtained by

3

means of rockets and satellites. The picture of the vertical structure of the ionosphere is now developing rapidly. Theories describing the properties of the ionosphere are also developing swiftly, and they aid in the analysis of ionospheric data from various sources. At extreme levels (altitudes of several Earth radii) ground measurements in the form of radio-whistler studies still provide the most definitive data, although space probes should soon supply valuable information in this region. The latitudinal variation in the structure of the ionosphere above the level of maximum ionization is not well known or understood. The nature of the irregularities and variations in the ionosphere also is not understood or well documented quantitatively.

Penetrating-particle radiation is at present a highly controversial field. There are widely differing viewpoints on the intensity of Van Allen radiation and of cosmic radiation originating in solar flares. The viewpoint presented here is that the intensities of Van Allen radiation-belt electrons and of solar-flare cosmic radiation are not nearly so high as many of the figures frequently quoted. The higher intensities of the Van Allen radiation-belt electrons are also presented, as the measurements are so ambiguous that the possibility that the higher intensities are actually present cannot be absolutely ruled out, although they are considered most unlikely. The controversy in the case of the Van Allen radiation is associated with differing ideas as to its origin. The early idea that it originates by capture of energetic electrons from the sun (solar injection) has been abandoned almost universally. A present widely held opinion is that the electrons are accelerated locally within the Earth's magnetic field. Another viewpoint, shared by a smaller group, is that these electrons originate principally through the decay of albedo neutrons leaving the Earth after having been released by the interaction of cosmic radiation with atmospheric nuclei. The intensities presented here are in agreement with this neutron-decay hypothesis.

Solar radiation has been studied for many decades and the total intensity is known within a few per cent. However, the ultraviolet radiation from the sun is not well known, as data in this spectral region can be obtained only at altitudes of 100 km and above. The entire ultraviolet spectrum has been observed by means of experiments performed in rockets, though the present data are rather tentative. Some measurements have been made of the X-rays from the sun, but no spectrum has been obtained up to the present time. Techniques are improving rapidly and it is clear that the intensity measurements and the spectral resolution in the ultraviolet and X-ray regions should improve rapidly in the next few years.

Data on micrometeorites are very sparse. A number of observations have been made from rockets and, especially, satellites. However, there is no truly satisfactory technique for calibrating the detectors in the laboratory, because of the difficulty in accelerating small particles to meteoric velocities. When a particle-acceleration technique is developed that will permit the calibration of micrometeorite detectors, the quality of the data can be expected to improve. Even without such accelerators, some improvement in detection techniques can be expected as more data are acquired with detectors based on different physical principles.

Satisfactory data have been obtained on radio noise. Working on the ground is not a disadvantage in such surveys except that extraterrestrial sources in the frequency region below a few megacycles cannot be observed, since these frequencies cannot penetrate the ionosphere. However, such measurements will probably be made above the ionosphere in the near future.

Thermal radiation from the Earth is very important in connection with the equilibrium temperatures attained by artificial Earth satellites. The radiation must be highly variable, depending on the meteorological situation. Data from thermal-radiation detectors in satellites will certainly be useful in this connection. Until such data are acquired, it is believed that the results from meteorological studies provide the best average values for the thermal radiation leaving the Earth, and values from such studies are presented here.

Magnetic data have been collected from observatories over the surface of the Earth for many decades. Analysis of such observations provides the description of the Earth's magnetic field given in this handbook. However, data from space probes and satellites are beginning to accumulate, and it is clear that these observations will be used to provide a detailed description of the outer portion of the Earth's field, where extrapolation from surface observations is clearly inadequate.

Supplementary data on the solar system, space probes and satellites, pertinent physical constants, and conversion factors have been included as an Appendix.

1

Structure of the Upper Atmosphere

Francis S. Johnson

1. Structure of the Upper Atmosphere / *Francis S. Johnson*

1.1. INTRODUCTION

The structure of the lower atmosphere in both position and time has been studied in considerable detail by meteorologists. However, as one examines higher and higher levels it is apparent that fewer and fewer data exist. Nevertheless, considerable information is available concerning the structure of the atmosphere to its outermost fringes. In this paper, we will concentrate attention on the higher levels and almost entirely ignore the region of meteorological interest.

On the basis of thermal structure, the atmosphere is divided into a number of regions. The lowest region, the troposphere, extends to an altitude of about 10 km over the poles and 16 km over the equator; this is essentially the region of meteorological interest. The upper boundary of the troposphere is the tropopause. Above the troposphere is the stratosphere, which has the stratopause as its upper boundary. There is some confusion as to the definition of the stratopause, but it is probably most satisfactory to consider it to be the temperature maximum which occurs near 50 km. Above the stratopause is the mesosphere, which extends to the temperature minimum near 80 km. (Frequently, the mesosphere is taken to be the broad region around the temperature maximum rather than just the upper half of it, as is suggested above.) Above the mesopause (the upper boundary of the mesosphere) is the thermosphere, in which the temperature rises rapidly to about 200 km and less rapidly above 200 km, becoming essentially isothermal above 400 km. Another region which is frequently mentioned is the exosphere, which is the upper portion of the thermosphere and is the region in which the atmospheric gas is so rarified that collisions between neutral particles can generally be neglected. The altitude of the base of the exosphere varies from 450 to 650 km during the solar cycle.

Many model atmospheres have been published; probably the most widely used of these is the ARDC 1959 atmosphere (Air Force Geophysics Research Directorate, 1960). The reasons for presenting still another model atmosphere

here rather than recommending the use of the ARDC atmosphere are: (1) that the great change in atmospheric structure that occurs during the solar cycle must be emphasized; and (2) that the model should incorporate the strongly probable concept that the upper atmosphere must be isothermal at altitudes considerably below and above the base of the exosphere, a concept not incorporated in the ARDC atmosphere.

1.2. ATMOSPHERIC RELATIONSHIPS

Because the sun heats the atmosphere nonuniformly, the physical properties of the atmosphere vary in space and time. Several equations relate these physical properties. Foremost among these is the hydrostatic relationship, which governs the vertical distribution of pressure. In differential form, the hydrostatic relationship is

$$dp = -\rho g dh, \tag{1-1}$$

where, at altitude h, p is the pressure, ρ is the atmospheric density, and g is the acceleration of gravity. This equation can also be expressed in the form

$$\frac{dp}{p} = \frac{-mg}{kT} dh = \frac{-dh}{H}, \tag{1-2}$$

where m is the average particle mass, T is the temperature at altitude h, k is the Boltzmann constant, and H is thè scale height. If m, g, and T are all constant, then H is the vertical distance over which the pressure changes by the factor e (the base of natural logarithms); it is defined by the expression

$$H = kT/mg. \tag{1-3}$$

When Eq. (1-2) is integrated, we obtain

$$p/p_0 = \exp\left[-\int_0^h (mg/kT)dh\right], \tag{1-4}$$

where p_0 is the pressure at an arbitrarily selected reference level at which h is assigned the value zero. By means of Eq. (1-4) the pressure ratio can be determined for any two levels between which the distributions of temperature and mean particle mass are known.

If the temperature and the average particle mass are constant with altitude, then, neglecting the variation of g with altitude, Eq. (1-4) simplifies to

$$p/p_0 = \exp(-h/H) = \exp(-mgh/kT). \tag{1-4'}$$

Further, $\rho/\rho_0 = n/n_0 = p/p_0$, where ρ and n are respectively the atmospheric density and particle concentration at altitude h, and ρ_0 and n_0 are the corresponding quantities at the reference level where $h = 0$. When the variation of g with altitude is taken into account we obtain, instead of Eq. (1-4'),

$$p/p = n/n_0 = \rho/\rho_0 = \exp\left[-mg_0 R_0 h/(R_0 + h)kT\right], \qquad (1\text{-}4'')$$

where R_0 is the distance from the center of the Earth to the reference level and g_0 is the acceleration of gravity at the reference level. Equation (1-4'') is one form of the generalized hydrostatic equation.

When the temperature and the average particle mass are not constant with altitude, Eq. (1-4) must be used instead of (1-4') or (1-4''). The corresponding equations for the density and particle concentration are

$$\rho/\rho_0 = (mT_0/m_0 T) \exp\left[-\int_0^h (mg/kT)\, dh\right] \qquad (1\text{-}5)$$

and

$$n/n_0 = (T_0/T) \exp\left[-\int_0^h (mg/kT)\, dh\right]. \qquad (1\text{-}6)$$

In Eq. (1-4), (1-5), and (1-6) the variation of temperature and mean particle mass must be known over the altitude region of concern, and the variation in g with altitude should be taken into account by using the relationship

$$g = g_0 R_0^2/(R_0 + h)^2. \qquad (1\text{-}7)$$

These are the most general forms of the equations expressing the relationships among the physical properties of the atmosphere and altitude.

The pressure may vary horizontally as well as vertically. When a horizontal pressure gradient exists, there is a tendency for the atmosphere to move horizontally in such a way as to equalize the pressure. Because of the rotation on the Earth, there is also a Coriolis force which deflects the movement to such an extent that the pressure-equalization flow is eventually stopped. In this limiting case, a balanced circulation is obtained in which the Coriolis and centrifugal forces associated with the circulation just balance the horizontal-pressure-gradient force. When the centrifugal force of the circulation due to the curvature of the particle trajectories is neglected, the balanced circulation can be computed by equating the Coriolis force to the pressure-gradient force. The wind calculated in this manner is known as the geostrophic wind, and the magnitude of its velocity is given by the equation

$$v = \frac{1}{2\rho \, \Omega \sin \lambda} \left| \nabla_H p \right|, \qquad (1\text{-}8)$$

where $\left| \nabla_H p \right|$ is the magnitude of the horizontal pressure gradient, Ω is the angular rate of rotation of the Earth, and λ is the latitude. It can also be expressed in the form

$$v = \frac{gs}{2\,\Omega\,\sin\lambda}\,, \qquad (1\text{-}8')$$

where s is the slope of the constant-pressure surface passing through the point in question. If the air motion is along a curved path, a centrifugal-force term should be added in Eq. (1-8) and the calculated wind, taking this force into account, is known as the gradient wind.

Although pressure differences occur over the Earth, with balanced circulations preventing pressure-equalization winds from annihilating the pressure differences, the variation in pressure at the Earth's surface is not very large. Extreme excursions amount to about ± 5 percent from the mean (ignoring tornadoes). At altitudes up to 100 km and somewhat above, the pressure distribution and the wind field are related by the gradient-wind equation; from the strength of the observed winds, it is clear that the pressure at given altitudes is relatively constant, although the relative variations are considerably larger than the ± 5 percent observed at the Earth's surface. At altitudes much in excess of 100 km, viscous forces play a prominent role and tend to prevent balanced circulations from occurring (Johnson, 1960), even though unequal heating must also occur in this altitude range. As a result, pressures are relatively constant over the Earth (*i.e.,* constant within a factor of less than 2) at altitudes near 200 km, because pressure-equalization flows greatly reduce the pressure variations which would otherwise occur.

1.3. ATMOSPHERIC DATA

Atmospheric temperature and pressure are measured directly in the troposphere by using instruments carried aloft with balloons, and the height of the observation is determined by using the hydrostatic equation, Eq. (1-1). However, as one moves well above the troposphere, it becomes difficult to measure temperature directly, because the temperature-measuring elements come into radiative equilibrium with their distant surroundings rather than into conductive equilibrium with their immediate surroundings. Consequently, at the lower rocket altitudes, the common practice is to measure pressure as a function of altitude or to determine the temperature from sound-velocity experiments using grenade sources carried aloft in rockets. Above altitudes of about 100 km, pressure becomes difficult to sense and sound does not propagate well, so density is the quantity more commonly observed as a function of altitude, the measurements generally being made either with vacuum gages which sense gas density or with satellites whose rate of orbital decay is observed.

The daytime atmospheric-temperature distribution is shown in **Fig. 1-1** for the extremes of the sunspot cycle. Below 100 km, there is no established varia-

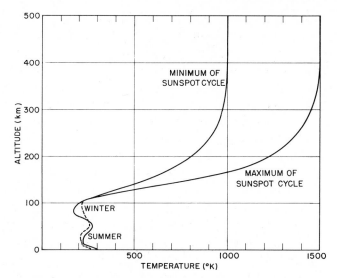

FIG. 1-1. Daytime atmospheric-temperature distribution at the extremes of the sunspot cycle. The solid curve applies at low and temperate latitudes in summer or winter and high latitudes in summer; the dashed curve applies at high latitudes in winter.

tion with the sunspot cycle; however, there is an appreciable seasonal variation at high latitudes. The temperature data below 30 km are averages from radiosonde balloons, and the values from 30 to 100 km are based largely on the rocket observations of Stroud *et al.* (1960). Other rocket data, mainly density measurements, are used at altitudes as high as 220 km. From 200 to 700 km, data from the orbital decay of satellites have been useful in defining the curve for sunspot maximum. The curve for sunspot minimum is based on rocket measurements up to 220 km and on some radio-ionospheric data at higher levels. The curve for sunspot maximum is in general agreement with atmospheric-density data presented by Harris and Jastrow (1959) and many others (*e.g.,* Jacchia, 1959; Kallmann, 1959, 1960; King-Hele, 1961; Martin and Priester, 1960; Siry, 1959). The curve for sunspot-cycle minimum is in general agreement with a pre-satellite analysis by Johnson (1958). The sharp rise in temperature between 100 and 200 km and the isothermal distribution above 300 or 400 km are in accordance with a theory originally put forth by Spitzer (1952) and further developed by Bates (1951) and Johnson (1956, 1958). More recently, other researchers have also adopted this concept on theoretical grounds (Nicolet, 1960), or on the basis of experimental evidence (Kallmann, 1960). The isothermal conditions shown in the upper portions of the curves in **Fig. 1-1** apply up to altitudes of several thousand kilometers, beyond which the average particle energy drops because some of the more energetic particles escape from the atmosphere.

Density data for daytime conditions are shown in **Fig. 1-2** for the altitude ranges 0 to 500 km and 0 to 2500 km. Two curves are shown, one for the period near the maximum of the sunspot cycle and the other for the period near the minimum. The density values up to 700 km for the sunspot-maximum curve are in good agreement with the data obtained from the orbital decay of satellites over the period September 1958 to February 1959; the atmospheric density at altitudes near 700 km has fallen considerably since that time. The curves above 700 km for sunspot maximum and above 220 km for sunspot minimum are extrapolated; the bends which occur near 1000 km for sunspot minimum and 2000 km for sunspot maximum are due to the presence of atomic hydrogen in the upper atmosphere.

The concentrations of the various atmospheric constituents at the extremes of the sunspot cycle are shown in **Fig. 1-3**. Mass-spectrometer measurements made in rocket flights at Churchill, Canada, have shown that diffusive equilibrium prevails above approximately 120 km (Meadows and Townsend, 1960); hence each component is distributed independently of the others and the vertical distribution of each component is just that which would prevail with the temperature distributions shown in **Fig. 1-1** with all the other components absent. Consequently, the shape of each of the curves shown can be calculated individually from the hydrostatic equation. The data on the concentrations of the various atmospheric constituents are tentative, as the only measurements which have been made are some molecular-oxygen measurements between 100 and 170 km (Byram *et al.*, 1955, 1957) and the total atmospheric-density measurements. The degree of oxygen dissociation has been estimated from these measurements, although Nicolet (1959) has pointed out the uncertainty involved in this procedure. No data at all exist for the relative concentrations of atomic and molecular nitrogen. The degree of nitrogen dissociation shown in **Fig. 1-3** has been selected on the basis of its apparent agreement with ion measurements near 700 km (Istomin, 1960; Poloskov, 1960). However, it has been pointed out (Hertzberg, 1961) that the ion composition may not be simply related to the neutral-particle composition. The relatively small degree of nitrogen dissociation shown in **Fig. 1-3** is in agreement with the generally prevailing opinion on this subject; however, there are also some reasons for believing that the nitrogen might be almost entirely dissociated above 200 km (Hertzberg, 1961).

The hydrogen concentrations around the Earth have been determined during the period of maximum sunspot activity (Johnson and Fish, 1960; Purcell and Tousey, 1960; Johnson, 1961); near sunspot-cycle minimum, the concentrations are probably higher, as indicated by the data shown in **Fig. 1-3**. The reason for the expected increase near the solar minimum is that the rate of supply of atomic

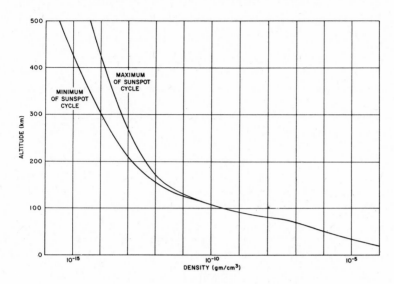

a. 0 to 500 km.

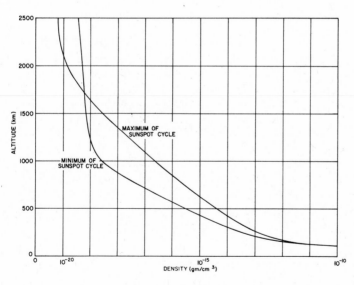

b. 0 to 2500 km.

FIG. 1-2. Average daytime atmospheric densities at the extremes of the sunspot cycle.

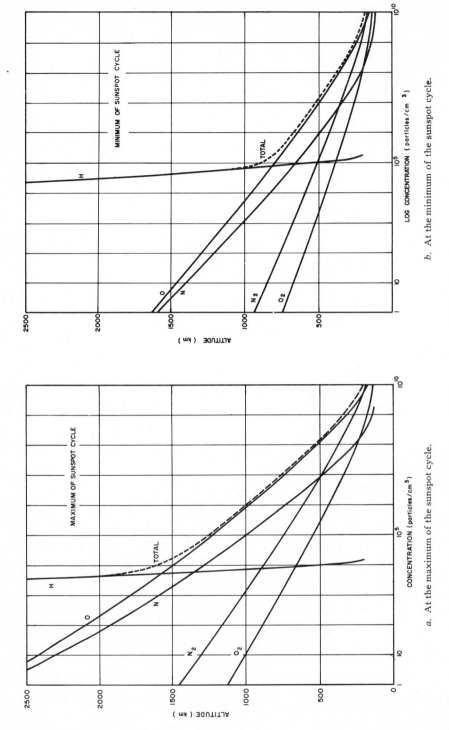

a. At the maximum of the sunspot cycle.

b. At the minimum of the sunspot cycle.

Fig. 1-3. Concentrations of the major atmospheric constituents. The total concentration of atmospheric particles is also shown.

hydrogen into the atmosphere, and hence its rate of escape from the atmosphere, should be nearly constant through the sunspot cycle. However, near sunspot minimum, the upper atmosphere is cooler and greater concentrations of atomic hydrogen must build up in order to maintain a constant escape flux.

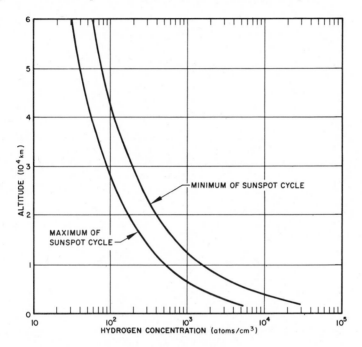

FIG. 1-4. Distribution of atomic hydrogen out to 60,000 km from the Earth at the extremes of the sunspot cycle.

The atomic-hydrogen concentrations expected farther from the Earth are shown in **Fig. 1-4**. The concentrations shown are based on the concept that, in addition to the atoms which are moving up from the base of the exosphere on ballistic orbits, substantial numbers of atoms are in orbit around the Earth (Johnson, 1961). There are doubts about the extent to which such orbits are populated by hydrogen atoms (Öpik and Singer, 1960), and the concentrations near 40,000 km would be lower by approximately a factor of 3 if there were only an insignificant number of hydrogen atoms in orbit. Although the concentrations in the lower exosphere are greater near sunspot minimum than near sunspot maximum, the concentration falls more rapidly with altitude with the lower temperature which prevails near sunspot minimum, therefore the concentrations at distances of the order of 50,000 km are more constant through the sunspot cycle than are the concentrations in the lower exosphere.

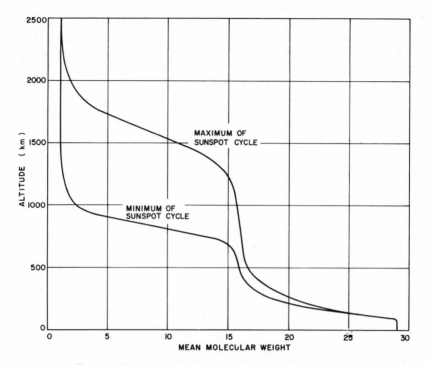

Fɪɢ. 1-5. Mean molecular weight as a function of altitude at the extremes of the sunspot cycle.

The mean molecular weight is shown as a function of altitude up to 2500 km in **Fig. 1-5**. The sudden decrease in molecular weight which occurs near 800 km at sunspot minimum and 1600 km at sunspot maximum is due to the presence of atomic hydrogen in the atmosphere. Below 100 km, the molecular weight rapidly approaches the value 29.0 that is applicable below 80 km.

The fractional atmospheric composition is indicated in **Fig. 1-6** for the region up to 500 km; the fractional portions of the atmosphere consisting of atomic and molecular oxygen and atomic and molecular nitrogen are shown for the extremes of the sunspot cycle. Over the altitude range shown, hydrogen remains a negligible fraction of the atmosphere. The horizontal distance between adjacent curves in **Fig. 1-6** is proportional to the relative concentration of the atmospheric constituent whose symbol appears between the curves.

Table 1-1 contains values of several of the atmospheric parameters shown in **Fig. 1-1** through **1-6** for the period of time near the maximum of the sunspot cycle. The scale height and the total concentration of atmospheric particles are also shown. Table 1-2 gives the same quantities for the period of time near the sunspot minimum; data for the altitude region below 100 km, which are not given in Table 1-2, are the same as in Table 1-1.

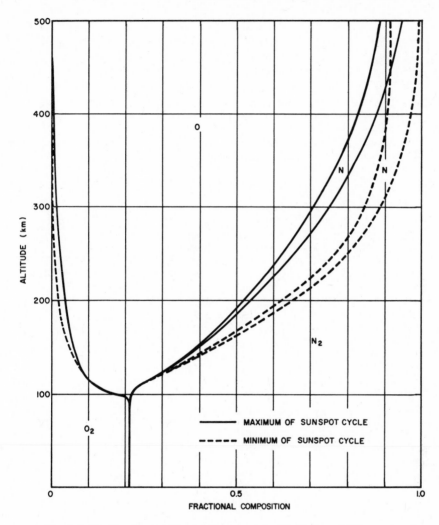

F_{IG}. 1-6. Fractional composition of the atmosphere (O, N, O_2, and N_2) as a function of altitude at the extremes of the sunspot cycle.

1.4.   ATMOSPHERIC VARIATIONS

It is recognized that the atmosphere is dynamic and that changes in it occur frequently. The data presented in the foregoing section represent average day-time conditions at low and temperate latitudes. Several variations from the pre-sented curves are to be expected. The largest variation is that which occurs during the sunspot cycle; the two models presented indicate the expected ex-tremes for this variation. Since solar ultraviolet radiation is thought to con-stitute the normal heat source in the ionosphere, the change in atmospheric

TABLE 1-1

ATMOSPHERIC PARAMETERS AS A FUNCTION OF ALTITUDE NEAR SUNSPOT MAXIMUM

The temperature T, molecular weight M, number concentration n, density ρ, pressure p, and scale height H are given as functions of altitude h.

h (km)	T (°K)	M	n (particles/cm³)	ρ (g/cm³)	p (dyne/cm²)	H (km)
0	288	29.0	2.5×10^{19}	1.22×10^{-3}	1.01×10^{6}	8.43
10	223	29.0	8.6×10^{18}	4.1×10^{-4}	2.65×10^{5}	6.56
20	217	29.0	1.85×10^{18}	8.9×10^{-5}	5.5×10^{4}	6.38
30	231	29.0	3.7×10^{17}	1.79×10^{-5}	1.19×10^{4}	6.83
40	261	29.0	8.3×10^{16}	4.0×10^{-6}	3.0×10^{3}	8.40
50	283	29.0	2.3×10^{16}	1.08×10^{-6}	9.0×10^{2}	8.11
60	245	29.0	7.53×10^{15}	3.7×10^{-7}	2.55×10^{2}	7.35
70	173	29.0	1.96×10^{15}	9.4×10^{-8}	4.7×10^{1}	5.21
80	168	29.0	2.84×10^{14}	1.36×10^{-8}	6.6×10^{0}	5.08
90	176	28.8	3.9×10^{13}	1.88×10^{-9}	9.5×10^{-1}	5.35
100	208	27.8	6.0×10^{12}	2.8×10^{-10}	1.74×10^{-1}	6.54
120	390	26.1	6.3×10^{11}	2.9×10^{-11}	3.4×10^{-2}	13.1
140	662	24.5	1.07×10^{11}	4.7×10^{-12}	1.04×10^{-2}	24.0
160	926	23.7	4.0×10^{10}	1.52×10^{-12}	5.1×10^{-3}	34.8
180	1115	22.8	2.0×10^{10}	7.7×10^{-13}	3.1×10^{-3}	43.6
200	1230	22.0	1.07×10^{10}	4.2×10^{-13}	1.95×10^{-3}	50.2
220	1305	21.2	6.6×10^{9}	2.7×10^{-13}	1.20×10^{-3}	55.3
240	1356	20.6	4.6×10^{9}	1.70×10^{-13}	8.5×10^{-4}	60.0
260	1400	20.0	3.3×10^{9}	1.12×10^{-13}	6.4×10^{-4}	63.8
280	1430	19.5	2.35×10^{9}	7.9×10^{-14}	4.7×10^{-4}	67.0
300	1455	19.1	1.82×10^{9}	5.7×10^{-14}	3.6×10^{-4}	70.6
320	1472	18.7	1.32×10^{9}	4.3×10^{-14}	2.7×10^{-4}	73.0
340	1485	18.4	1.00×10^{9}	3.1×10^{-14}	2.04×10^{-4}	75.6
360	1491	18.0	7.6×10^{8}	2.3×10^{-14}	1.54×10^{-4}	77.8
380	1496	17.8	5.9×10^{8}	1.78×10^{-14}	1.23×10^{-4}	79.9
400	1500	17.5	4.7×10^{8}	1.38×10^{-14}	9.8×10^{-5}	81.8
450	1500	17.0	2.5×10^{8}	7.2×10^{-15}	5.2×10^{-5}	85.7
500	1500	16.6	1.44×10^{8}	4.1×10^{-15}	2.9×10^{-5}	88.6
600	1500	16.3	4.8×10^{7}	1.32×10^{-15}	1.00×10^{-5}	93.1
700	1500	16.1	1.70×10^{7}	4.6×10^{-16}	3.5×10^{-6}	97.0
800	1500	16.0	6.3×10^{6}	1.66×10^{-16}	1.32×10^{-6}	101
900	1500	15.8	2.35×10^{6}	6.0×10^{-17}	4.9×10^{-7}	105
1000	1500	15.7	9.1×10^{5}	2.4×10^{-17}	1.90×10^{-7}	108
1200	1500	15.2	1.52×10^{5}	3.8×10^{-18}	3.2×10^{-8}	118
1400	1500	13.0	3.2×10^{4}	6.6×10^{-19}	6.7×10^{-9}	145
1600	1500	8.3	1.00×10^{4}	1.35×10^{-19}	2.1×10^{-9}	239
1800	1500	3.5	5.7×10^{3}	3.5×10^{-20}	1.14×10^{-9}	836
2000	1500	1.8	4.6×10^{3}	1.44×10^{-20}	9.5×10^{-10}	1167
2500	1500	1.0	3.47×10^{3}	6.0×10^{-21}	7.2×10^{-10}	2095

TABLE 1-2

ATMOSPHERIC PARAMETERS AS A FUNCTION OF ALTITUDE NEAR SUNSPOT MINIMUM

The temperature T, molecular weight M, number concentration n, density ρ, pressure p, and scale height H are given as functions of altitude h.

h (km)	T (°K)	M	n (particles/cm³)	ρ (g/cm³)	p (dyne/cm²)	H (km)
100	208	27.8	6.0×10^{12}	2.8×10^{-10}	1.74×10^{-1}	6.54
120	340	26.1	4.5×10^{11}	1.94×10^{-11}	2.1×10^{-2}	11.38
140	500	24.3	6.6×10^{10}	2.9×10^{-12}	4.6×10^{-3}	18.1
160	628	22.9	2.15×10^{10}	7.7×10^{-13}	1.86×10^{-3}	23.8
180	732	21.5	9.1×10^{9}	3.0×10^{-13}	9.1×10^{-4}	29.5
200	807	20.5	4.5×10^{9}	1.48×10^{-13}	5.0×10^{-4}	35.2
220	865	19.5	2.35×10^{9}	7.7×10^{-14}	2.8×10^{-4}	39.6
240	906	18.9	1.42×10^{9}	4.3×10^{-14}	1.77×10^{-4}	44.1
260	937	18.3	8.9×10^{8}	2.6×10^{-14}	1.14×10^{-4}	47.2
280	959	17.9	5.8×10^{8}	1.62×10^{-14}	7.6×10^{-5}	49.9
300	973	17.5	3.8×10^{8}	1.04×10^{-14}	5.1×10^{-5}	51.9
320	984	17.2	2.6×10^{8}	6.9×10^{-15}	3.5×10^{-5}	53.3
340	991	16.9	1.70×10^{8}	4.8×10^{-15}	2.34×10^{-5}	54.9
360	996	16.7	1.20×10^{8}	3.3×10^{-15}	1.66×10^{-5}	56.0
380	998	16.5	8.3×10^{7}	2.2×10^{-15}	1.14×10^{-5}	57.1
400	1000	16.3	6.0×10^{7}	1.58×10^{-15}	8.3×10^{-6}	58.4
450	1000	16.0	2.6×10^{7}	6.8×10^{-16}	3.6×10^{-6}	60.1
500	1000	15.9	1.20×10^{7}	3.1×10^{-16}	1.66×10^{-6}	61.6
600	1000	15.6	2.45×10^{6}	6.3×10^{-17}	3.4×10^{-7}	66.0
700	1000	14.7	5.8×10^{5}	1.28×10^{-17}	7.9×10^{-8}	76.0
800	1000	10.2	1.74×10^{5}	2.9×10^{-18}	2.4×10^{-8}	157
900	1000	5.1	9.1×10^{4}	1.38×10^{-19}	1.26×10^{-8}	312
1000	1000	2.3	7.1×10^{4}	3.7×10^{-19}	9.8×10^{-9}	487
1200	1000	1.3	5.3×10^{4}	1.07×10^{-19}	7.2×10^{-9}	915
1400	1000	1.0	4.5×10^{4}	7.6×10^{-20}	6.2×10^{-9}	1220
1600	1000	1.0	3.7×10^{4}	6.3×10^{-20}	5.1×10^{-9}	1319
1800	1000	1.0	3.1×10^{4}	5.6×10^{-20}	4.3×10^{-9}	1390
2000	1000	1.0	2.7×10^{4}	4.8×10^{-20}	3.8×10^{-9}	1456
2500	1000	1.0	2.0×10^{4}	3.4×10^{-20}	2.8×10^{-9}	1634

structure during the sunspot cycle indicates a substantial change in the solar ultraviolet radiation.

The next largest variation may well be the diurnal variation. Jacchia (1960) has deduced from satellite data that the density variations near 700 km amount to a factor of 10 between day and night; this would amount to a nighttime cooling of about 200°K in the isothermal region above 300 km. The actual magnitude of the diurnal variation remains in considerable doubt, however, because of the sparcity of data.

Another atmospheric-density variation of magnitude comparable to the diurnal variation is the day-to-day variation, which depends on the level of solar activity. Although these variations occur somewhat at random, they exhibit a tendency to recur with the period of solar rotation, or about 27 days. These variations have been correlated with the intensity of 20-cm solar radio noise (Priester and Martin, 1960). Nicolet (1960) has pointed out that the 20-cm radio-noise flux, which is observed regularly only in Berlin, does not correlate well with measurements of 3.2-, 8-, 10.7-, 15-, 21-, and 30-cm radiation, and that it therefore appears to contain a spurious variation. However, Jacchia (1960) claims that only the 20-cm measurements fit the satellite data well. There is no thought that the radio waves themselves affect the atmosphere; they are only an index of solar activity. It is possible that the mechanism which actually perturbs the atmosphere is the absorption of hydromagnetic wave energy (Dessler, 1959, Francis and Karplus, 1960). Under active solar conditions magnetic activity is increased, and the additional hydromagnetic heating above the normal solar ultraviolet heating causes the atmospheric density at high altitudes to increase.

Latitudinal variations are apparently fairly small, probably because of the importance of viscous forces in preventing balanced circulations from occurring (Johnson, 1960) ; in the absence of balanced circulations, horizontal motions

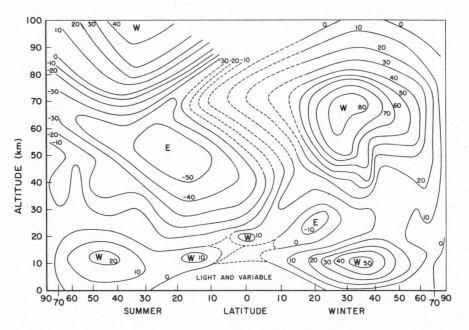

Fig. 1-7. Meridional cross section of the average zonal wind. Winds from the west (designated by W) are shown as positive; winds from the east (designated by E) are shown as negative. *Batten (1961), reproduced with permission of American Meteorological Society.*

can equalize the pressure along horizontal surfaces and the heat transport associated with this motion causes the temperature and density to equalize approximately also. It is unlikely that the latitudinal density differences between the equator and the poles are as large as a factor of 1.5 near 200 km, although they may be somewhat larger at higher altitudes. There is no satisfactory indication as to whether the density values over the polar regions are higher or lower than those over temperate latitudes, but they are probably lower. At altitudes below 120 km, where balanced circulations occur, the observed winds give an indication of the maximum latitudinal pressure differences which exist, and it appears unlikely that they are as large as a factor of 2. **Figure 1-7**, which is taken from a study by Batten (1961), indicates the strength of the average zonal wind. The geostrophic-wind equation, Eq. (1-8) or (1-8'), can be used to calculate latitudinal pressure differences from the winds shown in **Fig. 1-7**, and this indicates pressure differences amounting to a factor of less than 2, with low pressure and density in the mesosphere over the winter polar region. The wind structure over the equator (**Fig. 1-7**) is quite uncertain, as few data have been obtained there.

REFERENCES

Air Force Geophysics Research Directorate, 1960, *Handbook of Geophysics,* Macmillan, N.Y., pp. 1–1 to 1–43.

Bates, D. R., 1951, "The Temperature of the Upper Atmosphere," *Proc. Phys. Soc. (London), B,* **64,** 805–821.

Batten, E. S., 1961, "Wind Systems in the Mesosphere and Lower Ionosphere," (to be published in *J. Meteorol.,* **18**).

Byram, E. T., T. A. Chubb, and H. Friedman, 1955, "Dissociation of Oxygen in the Upper Atmosphere," *Phys. Rev.,* **98,** 1594–1597.

Byram, E. T., T. A. Chubb, and H. Friedman, 1957, "The Dissociation of Oxygen at High Altitudes," in *The Threshold of Space,* ed. M. Zelikoff, Pergamon Press, London, pp. 211–216.

Dessler, A. J., 1959, "Upper Atmosphere Density Variations Due to Hydromagnetic Heating," *Nature,* **184,** 261–262.

Francis, W. E., and R. Karplus, 1960, "Hydromagnetic Waves in the Ionosphere," *J. Geophys. Res.,* **65,** 3593–3600.

Harris, I., and R. Jastrow, 1959, "An Interim Atmosphere Derived from Rocket and Satellite Data," *Planet. Space Sci.,* **1,** 20–26.

Hertzberg, M., 1961, "Ion-Neutral Reactions" (to be published in *J. Atmos. Terrest. Phys.,* **19**).

Istomin, V. G., 1960, "An Investigation of the Ionic Composition of the Earth's Atmosphere Using Rockets and Satellites," *Artificial Earth Satellites,* Vol. 2, ed. L. V. Kurnosova, Plenum Press, New York, pp. 40–44.

Jacchia, L. G., 1959, "Solar Effects on the Acceleration of Artificial Satellites," Smithsonian Institution Astrophysical Observatory Special Report No. 29, Cambridge, Mass., September 21.

Jacchia, L. G., 1960, "A Variable Atmospheric-Density Model from Satellite Accelerations," *J. Geophys. Research,* **65,** 2775–2782.

Johnson, F. S., 1956, "Temperature Distribution of the Ionosphere Under Control of Thermal Conductivity," *J. Geophys. Research,* **61,** 71–76.

Johnson, F. S., 1958, "Temperatures in the High Atmosphere," *Ann. Geophys.,* **14,** 94–108.

Johnson, F. S., 1960, "Pressure and Temperature Equalization at 200-km Altitude," *J. Geophys. Research,* **65,** 2227–2232.

Johnson, F. S., 1961, "The Distribution of Hydrogen in the Telluric Hydrogen Corona," *Astrophys. J.,* **133,** 701–705.

Johnson, F. S., and R. A. Fish, 1960, "The Telluric Hydrogen Corona," *Astrophys. J.,* **131,** 502–515.

Kallmann, H. K., 1959, "A Preliminary Model Atmosphere Based on Rocket and Satellite Data," *J. Geophys. Research,* **64,** 615–623.

Kallmann, H. K., 1960, "Preliminary Day and Nighttime Model of the Atmosphere" (presented at the Helsinki meeting, IUGG, to be published in *J. Geophys. Research,* **66**).

King-Hele, D. G., 1961, "Properties of the Atmosphere Revealed by Satellite Orbits," (to be published in *Progress in the Astronautical Sciences,* Vol. 1, North-Holland Publishing Co., Amsterdam).

Martin, H. A., and W. Priester, 1960, "Measurements of Solar and Diurnal Effects in the High Atmosphere by Artificial Satellites," *Nature,* **185,** 600–601.

Meadows, E. B., and J. W. Townsend, 1960, "IGY Rocket Measurements of Arctic Atmospheric Composition above 100 km," *Space Research,* ed. H. Kallmann Bijl, North-Holland Publishing Co., Amsterdam, pp. 175–198.

Nicolet, M., 1959, "The Constitution and Composition of the Upper Atmosphere," *Proc. I.R.E.,* **47,** 142–147.

Nicolet, M., 1960, "Les variations de la densité et du transport de chaleur par conduction dans l'atmosphère supérieure," *Space Research,* ed. H. Kallmann Bijl, North-Holland Publishing Co., Amsterdam, pp. 46–89.

Öpik, E. J., and S. F. Singer, 1960, "Distribution of Density in a Planetary Exosphere," *Phys. Fluids,* **3,** 486–488.

Poloskov, S. M., 1960, "Upper Atmosphere Structure Parameters According to Data Obtained from U.S.S.R. Rockets and Satellites during IGY," *Space Research,* ed. H. Kallmann Bijl, North-Holland Publishing Co., Amsterdam, pp. 95–116.

Priester, W., 1959, "Sonnenaktivität und Abbremsung der Erdsatelliten," *Naturwissenschaften,* **46,** 197–198.

Priester, W., and H. A., Martin, 1960, "Solare und Tageszeitliche Effekte in der Hochatmosphäre und Beobachtungen an künstlichen Satelliten," Mitt. Sternwarte Bonn, No. 29 (Translation 901, Royal Aircraft Establishment, Farnborough, England).

Purcell, J. D., and R. Tousey, 1960, "The Profile of Solar Hydrogen-Lyman-α," *J. Geophys. Research,* **65,** 370–372.

Spitzer, L., Jr., 1952, "The Terrestrial Atmosphere above 300 km," *Atmospheres of the Earth and Planets,* ed. G. P. Kuiper, University of Chicago Press, Chicago, Ill., pp. 211–247.

Stroud, W. G., W. Nordberg, W. R. Bandeen, F. L. Bartman, and P. Titus, 1960, "Rocket Grenade Measurements of Temperatures and Winds in the Mesosphere over Churchill, Canada," *Space Research,* ed. H. Kallmann Bijl, North-Holland Publishing Co., Amsterdam, pp. 117–143.

2

Structure of the Ionosphere

W. B. Hanson

2. Structure of the Ionosphere / *W. B. Hanson*

2.1. INTRODUCTION

The radiation from the sun contains sufficient energy at short wavelengths to cause appreciable photo-ionization of the Earth's atmosphere at high altitudes. Thus the sun's radiation gives rise in the upper atmosphere to a partially ionized region known as the ionosphere. The recombination of the ions and electrons which are produced in this manner proceeds slowly enough at the low gas densities involved so that fairly high concentrations of electrons persist even throughout the night. During the daytime, several distinct ionospheric "layers" or "regions" are recognized, although the separation between them is not as distinct as was originally believed. In order of increasing altitude and increasing ion concentration, they are called the D, E, F_1, and F_2 regions. The different regions are identified in **Fig. 2-1**, which shows typical daytime and nighttime electron distributions as functions of altitude for the extremes of the sunspot cycle. The data apply for geomagnetic latitudes near 30 or 40 deg. Above the maximum electron concentration in the F_2 region, the electron concentration decreases monotonically out to several Earth radii, where the Earth's magnetic field and the protonosphere (the outermost portion of the ionosphere) are terminated by the solar wind or interplanetary plasma. Large diurnal effects occur, particularly in the lower ionosphere; these can be seen by comparing the daytime and nighttime curves in **Fig. 2-1**. The F_1 and F_2 regions join at night and the D region virtually disappears, the electron concentrations becoming too low to detect. The dependence of electron density on latitude is rather complicated and is not completely known or understood. Generally recognized features of this dependence will be described in the following discussions of the individual regions.

The electron concentration is essentially equal to the ion concentration everywhere in the ionosphere. There may be an exception to this equality in the D region at night, where electrons may combine with molecules to form negative

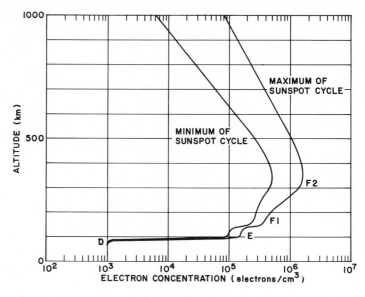

a. Daytime.

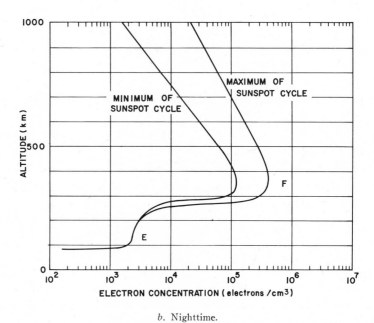

b. Nighttime.

FIG. 2-1. Normal electron distributions at the extremes of the sunspot cycle.

ions (negative ions are of no importance elsewhere in the ionosphere). Otherwise, through the lower ionosphere, the ion and electron concentrations are equal because they are created in pairs and eliminated in pairs. In the upper portion of the ionosphere, electric forces prevent any significant drift of one component relative to the other, thus keeping the concentrations of electrons and ions equal, although one species of ion may drift relative to another.

There is a generally accepted nomenclature for the properties of the different ionospheric regions—N_mD, N_mE, N_mF_1, and N_mF_2 denote the maximum electron concentrations in the D, E, F_1, and F_2 regions, respectively; h_mD, h_mE, h_mF_1 and h_mF_2 denote the heights of the peak concentrations in the various regions; and fD, fE, fF_1, and fF_2 are the critical frequencies for the peak electron concentrations, *i.e.*, they are the lowest radio frequencies which can penetrate the various regions at normal incidence. The maximum electron concentration is related to the critical frequency by the expression

$$N_m = 1.24 \times 10^4 f^2 \text{ electrons/cm}^3,$$

where f is expressed in megacycles per second. In plasma physics, the critical frequency is known as the plasma frequency, but critical frequency is the term usually used in ionospheric work.

2.2. THE D REGION

The D region is the lowest ionospheric region. The altitude usually ascribed to it is from 60 to approximately 85 km. It is thought that the ionizing agent is hydrogen Lyman-alpha radiation and that the primary ions formed are NO^+ (Nicolet, 1945; Bates, 1956), although no measurements of the ionic constituents have been made. Lyman-alpha radiation cannot ionize the principal atmospheric constituents, but it can ionize nitric oxide, which is a probable minor constituent of the atmosphere. The existence of traces of nitric oxide in the upper atmosphere, which would be sufficient to account for the presence of the D region, is considered probable (Nicolet and Aikin, 1960). Cosmic radiation also gives rise to some atmospheric ionization, and it makes a significant contribution to the lower portion of the normal D region. Measurements of D-region electron concentrations are very difficult to make with ground-based techniques; however, rocket flights have provided some unambiguous data on the electron concentrations (Seddon and Jackson, 1958). The maximum electron concentration occurs near 80 km and is of the order of 10^3 electrons/cm^3. The electrons essentially disappear at night, though the actual physical process involved is not well understood. Either recombination with positive ions or attachment to neutral particles to form negative ions may occur.

Because of the relatively high gas densities in the D region, electron collision frequencies there are high, and the region acts as a strong absorber of electromagnetic energy. At night, when the electron concentration is negligible, the attenuation of communication signals is much less than in the daytime. Three separate types of electromagnetic-absorption phenomena are associated with certain solar flares (Reid and Collins, 1959). The first of these is called the sudden ionospheric disturbance (SID). These events last for half an hour or so and are associated with increased ionization in the lower D region, which in turn gives rise to strong attenuation of radio signals, resulting in radio blackouts. The increased ionization occurs during the daytime and is caused by X-rays emitted by the sun (Friedman *et al.*, 1958a, 1958b). The second type of absorption is closely associated with active aurorae and magnetic disturbances. The absorption apparently takes place near the top of the D region and is predominantly a nighttime effect. At high latitude, *i.e.*, above the auroral zone, a third type of absorption takes place. These latter phenomena, called polar-cap blackouts, are caused by the penetration of energetic particles into the D region and below, following those flares which emit low-energy cosmic radiation (Bailey, 1959). The above absorption effects have sometimes been referred to as type I, type II, and type III absorptions, respectively. There is a strong positive correlation between all these effects and the 11-year sunspot cycle.

2.3. THE E REGION

The altitude range from approximately 85 to 140 km is designated the E region. It is now generally accepted that soft solar X-rays are mainly responsible for the photo-ionization which occurs in this altitude range (Bates, 1956; Friedman, 1959). The main ionic species, as shown by rocket-borne mass spectrometers (Johnson *et al.*, 1958; Istomin, 1960), are the diatomic ions O_2^+ and NO^+. NO^+ is the predominant ion except near 100 km during the daytime, when the two ion concentrations become comparable. With this exception, the concentration of NO^+ exceeds that of O_2^+ by at least a factor of 3. The primary ions that are formed are N_2^+, O_2^+, and O^+. The N_2^+ ions dissociatively recombine very rapidly (Faire and Champion, 1959), and they may also react chemically with oxygen, with the result that the concentration of N_2^+ is small. It was first recognized by Bates (1955) that ion-atom interchange reactions of the type

$$X^+ + YZ = XY^+ + Z$$

should proceed rapidly in the ionosphere. Such chemical reactions of O^+ with O_2 and N_2 quickly remove the O^+ ions and produce either NO^+ or O_2^+ ions in their place.

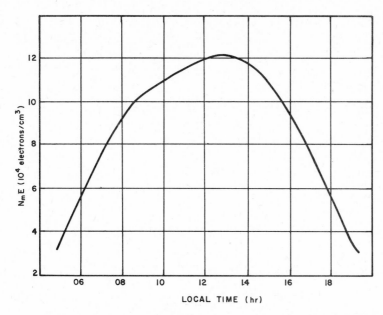

Fig. 2-2. Summer diurnal variation of $N_m E$ (maximum electron concentration in the E region) at Slough. *Appleton (1959), reproduced with permission of Institute of Radio Engineers.*

The electron concentration in the E region is of the order of 10^5 electrons/cm³ at noon during sunspot minimum and approximately 50 percent larger during sunspot maximum. The electron concentration is highest near local noon and falls off symmetrically with time on either side of noon, as shown in **Fig. 2-2**, where the summer diurnal variation of the maximum electron concentration in the E region at Slough, England, has been plotted (Appleton, 1959).

The variation of the noon values of the maximum electron concentration in the E region with time of the year at Washington, D.C., and Slough are plotted in **Fig. 2-3** (Appleton, 1959). The electron concentrations are roughly twice as large in summer as in winter at Slough, while the variation at Washington is not quite as large.

A rather common perturbation of the electron density in the E region occurs near 100 km and consists of a thin layer (only a few kilometers thick) in which the electron concentration may be as much as twice as high as the ambient concentration just above and below the layer (Seddon and Jackson, 1958). The layer is called Sporadic E. Another possible mechanism to account for the phenomenon of Sporadic E, which is evidenced by anomalous reflection characteristics, may be the existence of steep gradients in the electron concentrations. The temporal variations of Sporadic E are complicated and have been summarized in detail on a worldwide basis by Smith (1957). Sporadic E usually occurs

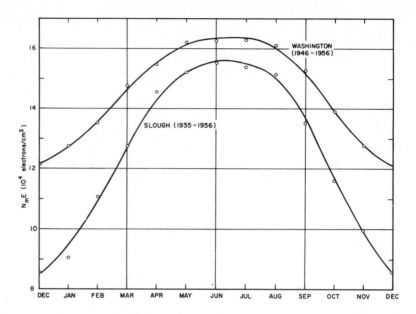

Fɪɢ. 2-3. Seasonal variations of monthly means of noon N_mE for Washington and Slough. Values were averaged over one sunspot cycle for Washington and over two for Slough. *Appleton (1959), reproduced with permission of Institute of Radio Engineers.*

at night at high latitudes and in the daytime near the magnetic equator. Throughout the temperate latitudes, the main variation is a seasonal one, with much more Sporadic E occurring during summer than winter.

2.4. THE F₁ REGION

The altitude demarcations between the E and F_1 regions and the F_1 and F_2 regions are not cleanly defined, and we shall arbitrarily call the altitude range from 140 to 200 km the F_1 region. The He II 304A line in the solar spectrum is principally responsible for the photo-ionization in this region, where several hundred electrons/cm³-sec are liberated (Hinteregger *et al.*, 1960). Because the photoelectrons are released with relatively high energy, which they share principally with other electrons, the electron temperature may be several hundred degrees higher than the ion temperature during the daytime (Hanson and Johnson, 1960). The predominant ions are NO^+ and O_2^+ near the low altitude boundary, and a gradual transition takes place until, at the upper boundary, O^+ is the principal ion (Johnson *et al.*, 1958). This is significant because of the greatly different recombination coefficients of the diatomic and monatomic ions, *i.e.*, about 10^{-8} cm³/sec and 10^{-12} cm³/sec, respectively. The electron concentration is typically of the order of 2.5×10^5 electrons/cm³ at noon during sunspot minimum and 4×10^5 electrons/cm^3 at noon during sunspot maximum. Large diurnal variations also occur in the F_1 region and the layer is not usually detected by ionosondes at night, when the electron density falls below 10^4 electrons/cm^3.

2.5.   THE F_2 REGION

Although $h_m F_2$, the altitude of the peak electron concentration in the F_2 region, changes considerably during the sunspot cycle, with latitude, and diurnally, we shall define the F_2 region as that lying in the altitude range from 200 to 1300 km, the lower limit being determined by the distribution of electron concentration and the upper limit by the change in ion composition from O^+ to H^+, which will be described in Section 2.6. The F_2 ionospheric region is probably the most difficult one to describe because of the many anomalies in its behavior (Martyn, 1959). The principal solar radiation responsible for the F_2-region ionization is probably the same as that for the F_1 region, *i.e.*, the He II 304A line. The reason a second ionization peak is formed is that the recombination rate falls off more rapidly with altitude than does the ionization rate, so that larger ion concentrations occur at higher altitudes. Ultimately, downward diffusion of ions becomes faster than either ionization or recombination and causes the ion concentrations to decrease with altitude.

Recent mass-spectrometer measurements in satellites (Istomin, 1960; Poloskov, 1960) show that the principal ions present are O^+ and N^+, with O^+ greatly predominant. Most of the monatomic ions do not recombine directly with electrons but react chemically with O_2 and N_2 to form O_2^+ and NO^+ ions, which then recombine relatively rapidly, as do the primary diatomic ions which are formed by photo-ionization. Thus the limiting processes for recombination are chemical ones, since the time for an O^+ ion to react with a neutral molecule is much longer than the recombination lifetime of the diatomic ion formed in the process. Since the concentration of neutral molecules falls off rapidly with altitude, so does the effective recombination coefficient change rapidly with altitude (Havens *et al.*, 1955), as it is of the order of 10^{-9} cm^3/sec at the base of the F_2 region, 10^{-10} cm^3/sec at $h_m F_2$ (the altitude of maximum electron density), and 10^{-12} cm^3/sec at some level well above $h_m F_2$.

The electron concentration at the F_2 peak varies in a complicated manner (Martyn, 1959); this behavior is shown in **Fig. 2-4**. Data for times near the equinoxes and near sunspot-cycle minimum and maximum are shown in **Fig. 2-4a** and **2-4b**. It can be seen that there is a high degree of symmetry between the two hemispheres, but that there is a peculiar relative minimum in the electron concentration during the afternoon over the geomagnetic equator. Data for times near the summer solstice and near sunspot-cycle minimum and maximum

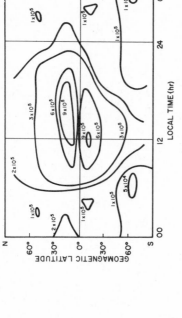

a. At equinox during sunspot minimum, 1943–44.

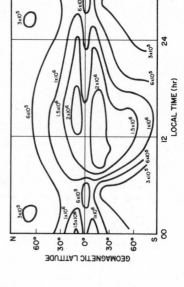

c. At summer solstice during sunspot minimum, 1943–44.

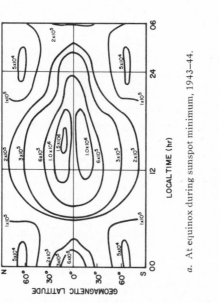

b. At equinox during sunspot maximum, 1947.

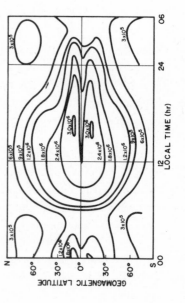

d. At summer solstice during sunspot maximum, 1947.

Fig. 2-4. Contours of $N_m F_2$ (electron concentrations at the F_2 peak) in electrons/cm³.

are shown in **Fig. 2-4c** and **2-4d**. The relative minimum in electron concentration over the geomagnetic equator is still clear, but the symmetry at high latitudes is disturbed by the tilt of the north polar region toward the sun.

The behavior of h_mF_2, the height of the maximum electron concentration, is extremely complicated; some of its variations are shown in **Fig. 2-5** and **2-6** (Thomas, 1959). **Figure 2-5** shows the change in h_mF_2 at three different stations as a function of local time at different times of the year and at high and low sunspot number; these data are for international quiet days (*i.e.*, days when the ionosphere is relatively undisturbed and in reasonable agreement with the models shown in **Fig. 2-1**). The height of the maximum electron concentration varies from 200 to 400 km at these medium-latitude stations. **Figure 2-6a** shows the latitude dependence of h_mF_2 averaged at noon and midnight over an equinox month at two epochs of the solar cycle. The average sunspot number, $\bar{R}$, is near zero at the minima of the solar cycles and usually between 50 and 200 at the maxima, the average being about 100. **Figure 2-6b** shows the same quantities during summer at noon and midnight at three epochs of the solar cycle. Generally speaking, at high latitudes h_mF_2 is higher at night than during the day while near the equator the opposite is true. Also, there is a general trend for h_mF_2 to increase with solar activity.

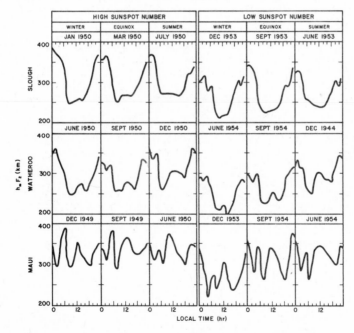

Fig. 2-5. Average variations of h_mF_2 (height of the F$_2$ peak) for 10 international quiet days in each month for three seasons in years of high and low sunspot number at three widely separated stations. *Thomas (1959), reproduced with permission of Institute of Radio Engineers.*

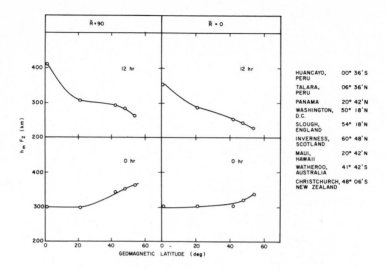

a. Averaged for an equinox month at two epochs of the sunspot cycle.

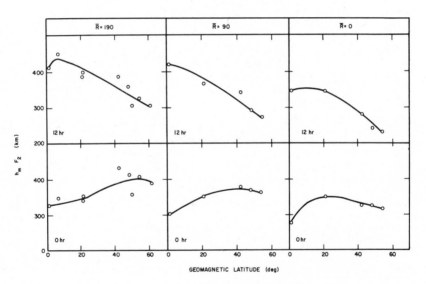

b. Averaged for a summer month at three epochs of the sunspot cycle.

FIG. 2-6. Variations of $h_m F_2$ with geomagnetic latitude.

Sometimes the F region shows a diffuse character which is attributed to clouds of electrons having concentrations different from the ambient surroundings. This condition is called "spread F," and it occurs mainly at night (Wright *et al.*, 1956). Since the dielectric constant of the ionosphere varies with the electron concentration, these inhomogeneities cause scintillation of signals from radio stars or other radio sources beyond the ionosphere. The phenomena of spread F occur more often at high latitudes during periods of high sunspot activity, show a minimum at all times near 35-deg geomagnetic latitude, and occur more often at low latitudes during periods of low sunspot activity.

2.6. THE PROTONOSPHERE

At approximately 1300-km altitude, the predominant ionic constituent changes from atomic oxygen ions to protons (Johnson, 1960). The scale height H, which is the altitude increment over which the ion concentration changes by a factor of e (see Eq. 1-4', Section 1.2), is inversely proportional to the effective ion mass. Thus, above 1300 km, the ion concentration falls off very slowly with altitude, the scale height H being greater than 2000 km. Johnson (1960) has suggested that this region be called the protonosphere to distinguish it from the lower ionized region (containing heavier ions) which is normally referred to as the ionosphere.

The concentrations of protons and oxygen ions in the transition region between the upper portion of the normal ionosphere and the protonosphere are shown in **Fig. 2-7a** for conditions near sunspot maximum; during this phase of the solar cycle, the transition is thought to occur at an altitude of about 1500 km (Hanson and Ortenburger, 1961). **Figure 2-7b** shows the transition region for conditions near sunspot minimum; the transition probably occurs near 1100 km under these conditions. The distribution of protons and electrons at altitudes well above the transition region is shown in **Fig. 2-8**, as deduced from observations of nose whistlers (Smith, 1960). Two curves are shown, one for periods near June and one for periods near December; the concentrations shown apply in the equatorial plane. There is no explanation for the annual variation exhibited by the protonosphere electron concentrations in the equatorial plane.

The solar radiation responsible for the formation of the protonosphere is the same as that for the upper portion of the F_2 region, the protons being formed by charge exchange between neutral hydrogen atoms and atomic oxygen ions, not by direct photo-ionization. This charge-exchange process takes place below a critical level near 800 km; below this level the proton density has a chemical-equilibrium distribution (Hanson and Ortenburger, 1961). Above the critical level, the protons obey a diffusive distribution law that depends on the concentrations and masses of the other ions present, which are mostly atomic oxygen ions. Effectively, the protons float on the heavier ions; their concentration increases with altitude up to approximately 1300 km, where the peak proton concentration reaches a value of approximately 5×10^3 protons/cm^3.

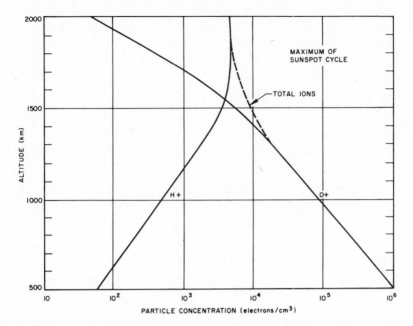

a. Near the maximum of the sunspot cycle.

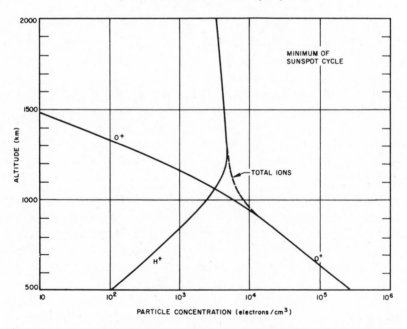

b. Near the minimum of the sunspot cycle.

FIG. 2-7. Ion concentrations in the transition region between the normal ionosphere and the protonosphere.

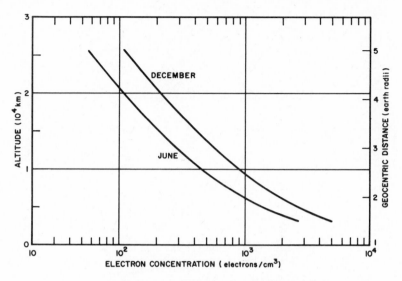

FIG. 2-8. Electron concentrations in the equatorial plane as a function of altitude, determined from nose-whistler data.

The slow diffusion rate of the protons through the ambient oxygen ions above the critical level prevents any effective coupling between the protonosphere and the F_2 region, therefore, the total number of protons in the protonosphere is fairly constant. Thus there are no large diurnal changes in the protonosphere even though the F_2 layer shows changes in ion concentration amounting to a factor of 5 or greater. The weak coupling between the protonosphere and the F_2 layer does not prevent the protonosphere from following the long-period changes in F_2 ion concentrations, *i.e.*, changes with season or solar cycle.

The protonosphere is the medium responsible for the propagation of radio whistlers. These low-frequency (1 to 30 kc) signals are generated by lightning strokes and follow paths along the Earth's magnetic field lines from one hemisphere to the other (Storey, 1953). They propagate at very large distances from the Earth and, at present, the main experimental evidence about the electron densities at great heights is provided by measurements of the dispersion of these waves; the data presented in **Fig. 2-8** were obtained from such studies (Smith, 1960).

2.7. IONOSPHERIC CONDUCTIVITIES AND COLLISION FREQUENCIES

The presence of electrons and ions in the ionosphere makes this atmospheric region electrically conducting. The concentrations of the charged particles and of the neutral particles govern the electrical conductivity, because collisions of

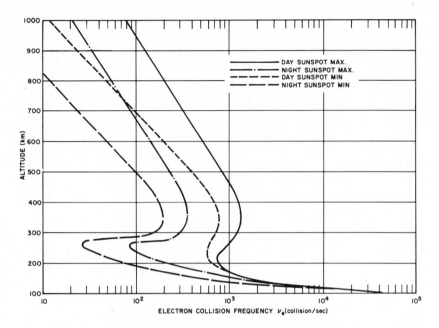

Fig. 2-9. Electron collision frequency ν_e versus altitude.

charged particles restrict their movement under the action of any impressed electric field. The presence of a magnetic field greatly complicates the problem, as it restricts the motion of the charged particles across the magnetic field and therefore makes the conductivity anisotropic. Several different electrical conductivities must be defined for use in the different physical situations which occur.

Nicolet (1953) has given expressions for the collision frequencies of electrons with ions and with neutral particles. The collision frequency of electrons with neutral particles is given by the expression

$$\nu_{en} = 5.4 \times 10^{-10} \, n_n T_e^{1/2} , \qquad (2\text{-}1)$$

where n_n is the concentration of neutral particles, and T_e is the electron temperature in degrees Kelvin. The expression

$$\nu_{ei} = [34 + 4.18 \ln \, (T_e^3/n_e)] \, n_e T_e^{-3/2} \qquad (2\text{-}2)$$

gives the collision frequency of electrons with ions. The electron-collision frequency with ions is much more temperature dependent than that with neutral particles, and in the opposite sense, because the collision cross section is highly dependent upon the velocity. The sum of the above two collision frequencies ν_{en} and ν_{ei} is plotted in **Fig. 2-9** as the electron collision frequency ν_e.

An expression for the frequency of collisions between ions and neutral particles was given by Chapman (1956) as

$$v_i = 2.6 \times 10^{-9} \, (n_n + n_i) \, M^{-1/2} \,, \qquad (2\text{-}3)$$

where n_i is the ion concentration and M is the molecular weight of the ions and neutral particles, which are assumed to have the same mass. This collision frequency is not temperature dependent, because the collision cross section varies inversely as the relative velocity. The collision frequency depends on the product of the velocity and the cross section; thus it is velocity independent and therefore also temperature independent. One does not need to consider ion collisions with electrons; the electrons are so light that the ions essentially are not affected by encounters with electrons (although the electrons, of course, are greatly affected by their encounters with ions). The calculated collision frequencies for ions are shown in **Fig. 2-10**. The values of M as a function of altitude were taken from Tables 1-1 and 1-2.

The specific electrical conductivity is that which exists parallel to a magnetic field or in the absence of a magnetic field, so it is often referred to as the zero-field conductivity. It is given by the expression

$$\sigma_0 = ne^2 \left[\frac{1}{m_e(v_e - i\omega)} + \frac{1}{m_i(v_i - i\omega)} \right], \qquad (2\text{-}4)$$

where e is the electronic charge $(1.6 \times 10^{-20}$ emu$)$, n is the electron (or ion) concentration, m_e and m_i are the electron and ion masses, respectively, and ω

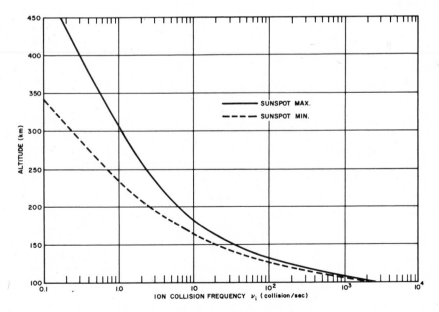

FIG. 2-10. Ion collision frequency v_i versus altitude.

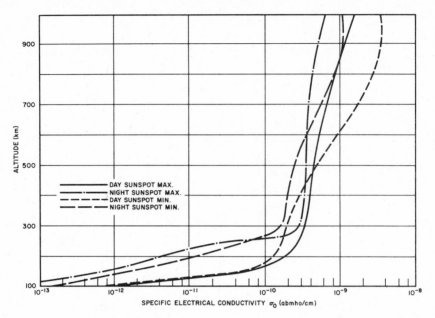

Fig. 2-11. Specific electrical conductivity σ_0 (zero-field conductivity) versus altitude.

is the impressed or driving frequency. Setting ω equal to zero and using data from **Fig. 1-1, 1-2, 2-1**, and **2-2**, we computed the specific electrical conductivity as a function of altitude. The result is shown in **Fig. 2-11** for the extremes of the sunspot cycle and for daytime and nighttime. These data apply along the direction of the magnetic field if one is present or in problems where there is no magnetic field, provided the collision frequency is large compared with the impressed frequency.

The Pederson conductivity is that which applies perpendicular to the direction of the magnetic field when one is present. It is sometimes referred to as the reduced conductivity because the presence of the magnetic field lowers the specific electrical conductivity (or zero-field conductivity) for problems involving the component of an electric field which is perpendicular to the magnetic field. The Pederson conductivity is given by the expression

$$\sigma_1 = ne^2 \left\{ \frac{\nu_e - i\omega}{m_e[(\nu_e - i\omega)^2 + \omega_e^2]} + \frac{\nu_i - i\omega}{m_i[(\nu_i - i\omega)^2 + \omega_i^2]} \right\}, \qquad (2\text{-}5)$$

where ω_e and ω_i are the electron and ion cyclotron frequencies, given respectively by Be/m_e and Be/m_i. The conductivities shown in **Fig. 2-12** were obtained with the same data as before. These conductivities are the ones to be used to compute the electric current in the direction of the component of an impressed electric field that is perpendicular to the magnetic field.

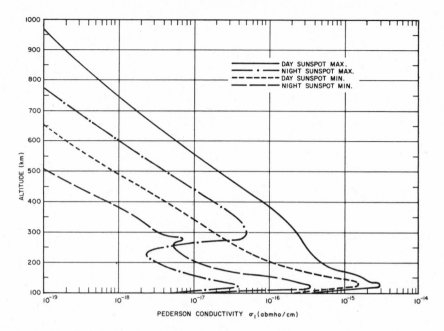

DAY SUNSPOT MAX.
NIGHT SUNSPOT MAX.
DAY SUNSPOT MIN.
NIGHT SUNSPOT MIN.

PEDERSON CONDUCTIVITY σ_1(abmho/cm)

FIG. 2-12. Pederson conductivity σ_1 (reduced conductivity) versus altitude.

When an electric field **E** is applied in the presence of a magnetic field **B**, charged particles tend to drift in the direction **E** × **B**, which is perpendicular to the two fields. In the absence of collisions, the positive and negative particles drift at the same speed and no current results. When collisions occur, the motions of the electrons and the ions are usually restricted in different degrees and a current results; this current is known as the Hall current. The conductivity used in computing this current is known as the Hall conductivity, which is given by the expression

$$\sigma_2 = ne^2 \left\{ -\frac{\omega_e}{m_e[(v_e - i\omega)^2 + \omega_e^2]} + \frac{\omega_i}{m_i[(v_i - i\omega)^2 + \omega_i^2]} \right\}. \quad (2\text{-}6)$$

The conductivities shown in **Fig. 2-13** were obtained with the same data as before. These conductivities are to be used to compute the currents which flow in directions perpendicular to both the electric and magnetic field.

The Cowling conductivity, a combination of the Pederson and Hall conductivities, is useful in computing energy dissipation associated with currents in plasmas. The energy loss per unit volume due to a current flowing in a direction perpendicular to the magnetic field is given by j^2/σ_3, where j is the current density and σ_3 is the Cowling conductivity. In general, the current flow is not in the direction of the applied electrical field but has components due to both the Pederson conductivity σ_1 and the Hall conductivity σ_2. Since the energy

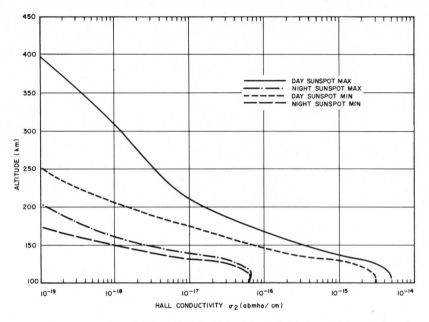

FIG. 2-13. Hall conductivity σ_2 versus altitude.

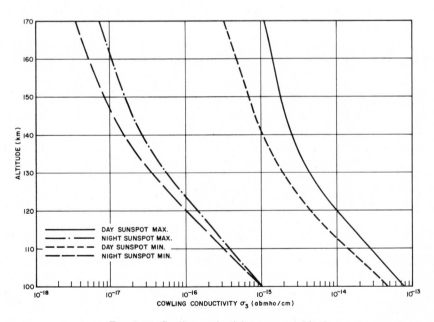

FIG. 2-14. Cowling conductivity σ_3 versus altitude.

dissipation per unit volume is given by either j^2/σ_3 or $\mathbf{j} \cdot \mathbf{E}$, it follows that

$$\sigma_3 = \sigma_1 + \sigma_2{}^2/\sigma_1. \tag{2-7}$$

The conductivities shown in **Fig. 2-14** were obtained with the previous data. Above 170 km, the Cowling conductivity is not significantly different from the Pederson conductivity.

The expressions given above for the various conductivities were taken from Francis and Karplus (1960). The values for the collision frequencies and conductivities presented above were calculated by W. E. Francis. A complete treatment of the fundamental physics involved has been given by Chapman and Cowling (1939), and a lucid discussion of the entire ionospheric conductivity problem has been given by Chapman (1956).

The conductivities given in **Fig. 2-11** through **2-14** have been calculated for ω equal to zero, or for quasi-steady-state conditions, where the applied electric field does not change significantly in a time comparable to the various collision frequencies. However, Eq. (2-4) to (2-7) can be used to compute the conductivities when the impressed frequencies are comparable to, or greater than, the collision frequencies.

REFERENCES

Appleton, E. V., 1959, "The Normal E Region of the Ionosphere," *Proc. I.R.E.*, **47**, 155–159.

Bailey, D. K., 1959, "Abnormal Ionization in the Lower Ionosphere Associated with Cosmic-Ray Flux Enhancements," *Proc. I.R.E.*, **47**, 255–266.

Bates, D. R., 1955, "Charge Transfer and Ion-Atom Interchange Collisions," *Proc. Phys. Soc. (London), A*, **68**, 344–345.

Bates, D. R., 1956, "Formation of the Ionized Layers," *Solar Eclipses and the Ionosphere*, ed. W. J. G. Beynon and G. M. Brown, Pergamon Press, London, pp. 184–188.

Chapman, S., 1956, "The Electrical Conductivity of the Ionosphere: a Review," *Nuovo cimento*, **4**, suppl., 1385–1412.

Chapman, S., and T. G. Cowling, 1939, *The Mathematical Theory of Non-Uniform Gases*, Cambridge University Press.

Faire, A. C., and K. S. W. Champion, 1959, "Measurements of Dissociative Recombination and Diffusion in Nitrogen at Low Pressures," *Phys. Rev.*, **113**, 1–6.

Francis, W. E., and R. Karplus, 1960, "Hydromagnetic Waves in the Ionosphere," *J. Geophys. Research*, **65**, 3593–3600.

Friedman, H., 1959, "Rocket Observations of the Ionosphere," *Proc. I.R.E.*, **47**, 272–280.

Friedman, H., T. A. Chubb, J. E. Kupperian, and J. C. Lindsay, 1958a, "X-ray and Ultraviolet Emission of Solar Flares," *I.G.Y. Rocket Report Series 1*, IGY World Data Center A, National Academy of Sciences, Washington, pp. 179–182.

Friedman, H., T. A. Chubb, J. E. Kupperian, and J. C. Lindsay, 1958b, "X-ray Emission of Solar Flares," *I.G.Y. Rocket Report Series 1*, IGY World Data Center A, National Academy of Sciences, Washington, pp. 183–185.

Hanson, W. B. and F. S. Johnson, 1960, "Electron Temperatures in the Ionosphere," Tenth International Astrophysical Colloquium, Liége, Belgium (to be published in *Mémoires, Soc. Roy. Sci., Liége*).

Hanson, W. B., and I. Ortenburger, 1961, "The Coupling Between the Protonosphere and the Normal F Region" (to be published in *J. Geophys. Research, 66*).

Havens, R. J., H. Friedman, and E. O. Hurlburt, 1955, "The Ionospheric F_2 Region," *The Physics of the Ionosphere,* The Physical Society, London, pp. 237–244.

Hinteregger, H. E., K. R. Damon, L. Heroux, and L. A. Hall, 1960, "Telemetering Monochromator Measurements of Solar 304 A Radiation and Its Attenuation in Upper Atmosphere," *Space Research,* ed. H. Kallmann Bijl, North-Holland Publishing Co., Amsterdam, pp. 615–627.

Istomin, V. G., 1960, "An Investigation of the Ionic Composition of the Earth's Atmosphere Using Rockets and Satellites," *Artificial Earth Satellites,* Vol. 2, ed. L. V. Kurnosova, Plenum Press, New York, pp. 40–44.

Johnson, C. Y., E. B. Meadows, and J. C. Holmes, 1958, "Ion Composition of the Arctic Ionosphere," *J. Geophys. Research, 63,* 443–444.

Johnson, F. S., 1960, "The Ion Distribution above the F_2 Maximum," *J. Geophys. Research, 65,* 577–584.

Martyn, D. F., 1959, "The Normal F Region of the Ionosphere," *Proc. I.R.E., 47,* 147–155.

Nicolet, M., 1945, "Contribution à l'étude de la structure de l'ionosphère," *Inst. Roy. Météor., Belgique, Mémoires, 19,* 124.

Nicolet, M., 1953, "The Collision Frequency of Electrons in the Ionosphere," *J. Atmos. Terrest. Phys., 3,* 200–211.

Nicolet, M., and A. C. Aikin, 1960, "The Formation of the D Region of the Ionosphere," *J. Geophys. Research, 65,* 1469–1483.

Poloskov, S. M., 1960, "Upper Atmosphere Structure Parameters According to Data Obtained from U.S.S.R. Rockets and Satellites during IGY," *Space Research,* ed. H. Kallmann Bijl, North-Holland Publishing Co., Amsterdam, pp. 95–116.

Reid, G. C., and C. Collins, 1959, "Observations of Abnormal VHF Radio Wave Absorption at Medium and High Latitudes," *J. Atmos. Terrest. Phys., 14,* 63–81.

Seddon, J. C., and J. E. Jackson, 1958, "Ionospheric Electron Densities and Differential Absorption," *Ann. Geophys., 14,* 456–463.

Smith, E. K., 1957, "Worldwide Occurrence of Sporadic E," National Bureau of Standards Circular No. 582.

Smith, R. L., 1960, "The Use of Nose Whistlers in the Study of the Outer Ionosphere," Technical Report No. 6, Contract AF18(603)-126, Stanford Electronics Laboratories, Stanford, Calif.

Storey, L. R. O., 1953, "An Investigation of Whistling Atmospherics," *Phil. Trans. Roy. Soc. (London), A, 246,* 113–141.

Thomas, J. O., 1959, "The Distribution of Electrons in the Ionosphere," *Proc. I.R.E., 47,* 162–175.

Wright, R. W., J. R. Koster, and N. J. Skinner, 1956, "Spread F Layer Echoes and Radio-Star Scintillation," *J. Atmos. Terrest. Phys., 8,* 240–246.

3

Penetrating Radiation

A. J. Dessler

3. Penetrating Radiation / *A. J. Dessler*

3.1. INTRODUCTION

The radiations that will be described in this chapter are those which can penetrate at least a few milligrams per square centimeter of material. The surface of the Earth is protected from most of the penetrating radiation found in space by the atmosphere, which constitutes approximately 10^3 g/cm^2 of shielding. The geomagnetic field exerts a major influence on charged-particle radiation near the Earth. Therefore the intensity of radiation around the Earth will, in general, be altitude-dependent and the charged-particle component will also show a latitude dependence. The penetrating radiations that a rocket or satellite vehicle encounters are, with a few exceptions, unobservable at the Earth's surface. Thus such vehicles are required to investigate the space-radiation environment. For example, the existence of the Van Allen radiation belt—the most intense penetrating-radiation flux now known to be present in space—was not even suspected before it was discovered in 1958 by means of the Explorer I satellite system, which actually penetrated well into the radiation belt.

Most of the data on penetrating radiation were obtained during the past two or three years; many critical parameters—particularly the energy spectra—are poorly known. We may expect that definitive experiments will soon be performed that will fill in many gaps in our knowledge of penetrating space radiation.

3.2. VAN ALLEN RADIATION

The most intense penetrating radiation now known to be present in space lies within the Van Allen radiation belt. This radiation consists of high-energy charged particles (both electrons and protons) that are trapped in the Earth's magnetic field.

In order to understand the nature of the Van Allen radiation, it is necessary first to understand the motion of an individual charged particle trapped in a dipole-like field; this motion is discussed in Section 3.2.1. In Sections 3.2.2 through 3.2.5 the Van Allen radiation belt itself will be described.

3.2.1. Motion of a Charged Particle Trapped in the Geomagnetic Field

The Van Allen radiation belt is a band of energetic-particle radiation trapped in the geomagnetic field. An excellent discussion of the physics of particles trapped in a dipole field has been given by Alfvén (1950). A brief description of the particle motion is given below, but the reader is referred to Alfvén's book and a paper by Northrup and Teller (1960) for detailed derivations and other pedagogical points.

A charged particle trapped in the geomagnetic field executes a complex motion. However, this complex motion can be divided into three simple components that are described below.

1. A particle moves in a circle of radius $a = mv \, c/(ZeB)$ with an angular frequency $\omega_c = ZeB/(mc)$, where m is the mass of the particle, v is its component of velocity perpendicular to the local magnetic-field direction, c is the velocity of light, Ze is the particle charge in esu, and B is the magnitude of the local magnetic field in gauss. For Van Allen radiation particles $a \ll r$, where r is the distance to the center of the Earth from the magnetic-field line about which the particle is spiraling. This circular motion is properly called cyclotron motion; a is the cyclotron radius and ω_c is the cyclotron frequency. The center of the circle is called the particle's guiding center.

2. The guiding center of a particle whose velocity vector makes an angle α (the pitch angle) with the magnetic-field direction at a position where the field strength is B moves almost parallel to the field line to a position where the field strength is $B_m = B/\sin^2\alpha$, where B_m is the maximum field strength to which the particle can penetrate. The position at which $B = B_m$ is called the mirror point, since a particle reaching this point will be reflected back along the field line. Thus the guiding center of a particle trapped in the geomagnetic field moves very nearly parallel to a field line (see 3 below) and bounces back and forth between northern- and southern-hemisphere mirror points.

3. As a trapped particle bounces back and forth between mirror points, its guiding center slowly drifts in longitude; positively charged particles drift westward and negatively charged particles drift eastward. The particle's guiding center traces out a magnetic shell that, in a perfect dipole field, would lie on a surface defined by the figure of revolution of a magnetic-field line. A magnetic-field line in a dipole field is given by

$$r = b \cos^2 \lambda_m \,.$$

where r is the geocentric distance to a point on the magnetic-field line, b is the geocentric distance at which the field line crosses the equatorial plane, and λ_m is the angle between the equator and r (*i.e.,* the magnetic latitude).

The above description of the motion of a particle trapped in a magnetic field applies for an undistorted dipole. In a field which is slightly distorted (as is the Earth's field) the situation is somewhat more complicated and invariants of the motion are required to describe the motion exactly.

Three invariants describe the motion of a charged particle trapped in a static magnetic field. Each of these invariants will be described briefly with respect to the Van Allen radiation belt. For a more detailed discussion, with many references to previous work on this subject, see Northrup and Teller (1960). The three invariants are as follows:

1. The first invariant is the adiabatic or magnetic-moment invariant. The magnetic moment of a charged particle in a magnetic field is given by $\mu = \frac{1}{2} mv_\perp^2/B$, where m is the mass of the particle, $v_\perp$ is its component of velocity perpendicular to the local magnetic-field direction, and B is the magnitude of the local magnetic field. As long as the particle motion and field configuration are such that the magnetic-field strength changes only very slightly over the distance the particle moves in one cyclotron period, the magnetic moment remains constant, *i.e.,* $v_\perp^2/B$ is a constant of the motion.

2. The second invariant is the integral or longitudinal invariant. The integral invariant is given by $J = \oint v_\parallel dl$, where $v_\parallel$ is the component of the particle velocity parallel to the local magnetic field, dl is the element of length along the line of force, and the integral is evaluated between mirror points. This invariant of the motion places an additional constraint on the motion of a trapped particle. If a trapped particle drifts in the geomagnetic field so that μ and J are constant, the particle must drift in such a way that it eventually returns to the same field line from which it started. The constancy of μ requires only that B_m be constant; the additional constancy of J requires that the particle drift along a well defined integral-invariant surface. One of the useful and instructive results of the integral-invariant calculation is shown in **Fig. 3-1**, in which the integral-invariant calculations of Jensen *et al.* (1960) are used to indicate some paths or traces that would be described by the mirror points of particles trapped in the geomagnetic field. The trace labeled 0 is the magnetic-invariant equator, *i.e.,* the path of a drifting particle whose northern and southern mirror points are coincident, or whose pitch angle is 90 deg. The remaining traces are conjugate traces, *i.e.,* the corresponding traces in the northern and southern (geomagnetic) hemi-

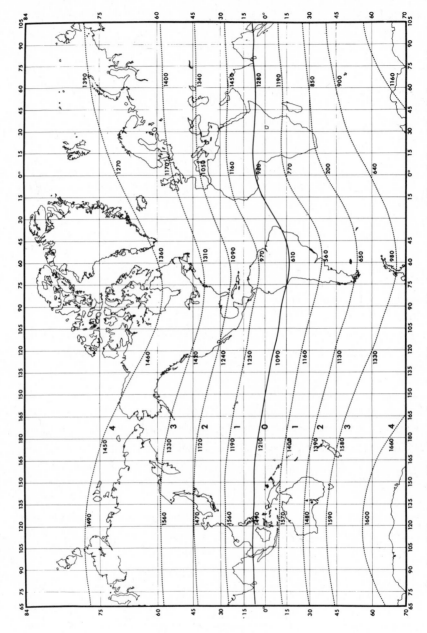

Fig. 3-1. Paths described by mirror points of particles trapped in the geomagnetic field, as indicated by the integral invariant. Trace 0 is the integral-invariant equator. Traces labeled 1, 2, 3, and 4 are conjugate traces. Mirror altitudes, arbitrarily chosen to be near 1500 km at 120° E longitude, are given at 60° intervals along each trace.

spheres followed by mirror points of selected particles. Mirror-point altitudes are shown along the traces for particles which were arbitrarily selected
to have mirror points at altitudes near 1500 km in the vicinity of 120° E.
longitude.

3. The third invariant is the flux invariant, which is simply the magnetic flux
inside the integral-invariant surface defined in 2. That is, the flux invariant
Φ is given by

$$\Phi = \int_s \mathbf{B} \cdot d\mathbf{s} ,$$

where $d\mathbf{s}$ is an element of area. The integral is evaluated over any surface
joining the magnetic equator of the Earth to the integral-invariant surface.
The constancy of Φ requires that, if the geomagnetic field were slowly to
contract or expand (as happens during some phases of geomagnetic storms),
the integral-invariant surface must change its size accordingly so that Φ is
conserved. During this process, μ and J also remain constant. An alternate
way of stating the flux invariant is that the drifting particle follows slow
movements of the magnetic field.

3.2.2.   Description of the Van Allen Radiation Belt

At the present writing, our knowledge of the electron component of the Van
Allen radiation belt is quite inadequate except to give a highly tentative description. When the results of definitive experiments are available, it will be possible
to present many additional data along with any required revisions of the current
estimates. The following description represents the author's best estimates of
the features of the radiation belt. Major areas of uncertainty and controversy
will be indicated.

The Van Allen radiation belt has been shown to consist of two components:
(1) a hard-proton component (the proton belt) centered at approximately
10×10^3 km from the Earth's magnetic axis (Freden and White, 1959; Fan
et al., 1960); and (2) an electron component (the electron belt) centered at
approximately 22×10^3 km from the Earth's magnetic axis (Van Allen, 1959;
Vernov *et al.*, 1959a; Walt *et al.*, 1960; Fan *et al.*, 1960; Arnoldy *et al.*, 1960a).
The electron belt extends through the region occupied by the proton belt (Holly
and Johnson, 1960). A sketch of particle flux versus altitude in the equatorial
plane is shown in **Fig. 3-2**. This sketch is based principally on the work of
Freden and White (1959, 1960) and McIlwain (1959), which established that
the penetrating component of the inner zone (sometimes also called the inner
belt) consists of hard protons, and the work of Vernov *et al.* (1959a) and Walt
et al. (1960), which established that the penetrating radiation of the outer zone

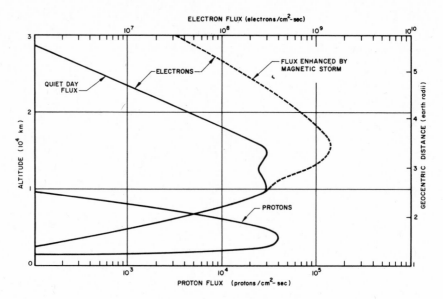

Fɪɢ. 3-2. Van Allen radiation-belt particle flux versus altitude in the equatorial plane.

(or belt) is composed of electrons. The spatial distribution of the protons and electrons shown in **Fig. 3-2** is based primarily on the measurements of Fan *et al.* (1960). The shape of the electron curve is very uncertain, with the possibility existing that the electron flux in the inner zone is as great as the electron flux in the outer zone (McIlwain, private communication). The relative minimum in the radiation belt as detected by the space probe Pioneer III is interpreted as the gap between the proton belt and the high-intensity region of the electron belt.

Observations have shown that the electron belt undergoes changes which are associated with geomagnetic storms (Van Allen and Frank, 1959b; Fan *et al.,* 1960; Rosen *et al.,* 1960; Arnoldy *et al.,* 1960a). After the active part of the storm (see Section 8.5) was over, the counting rate of instrumentation flown through the outer part of the electron belt increased in a manner somewhat as shown by the dashed electron curve in **Fig. 3-2**. The magnitudes and times of occurrence of these variations depended on the type of detector used and the characteristics of the particular geomagnetic storm. Following the active phase of the storm of 16 August 1959, the counters in Explorer VI showed a typical increase of about a factor of 5 near the middle of the electron belt. The storm of 2 September 1959 apparently had a much smaller effect on the observed counting rate of Explorer VI instruments in the electron belt. After the enhancement of the apparent intensity of the radiation belt by a magnetic storm, the belt returns to its pre-storm or quiet-day intensity.

Another example of possible time variations in electron-belt intensity is shown by measurements made with apparently identical instruments (Anton type 302 Geiger counters with about 1 gm/cm² of shielding) in the space probe Pioneer IV and the satellite Explorer VI. The difference between the counting rate at the peak of the electron belt for Pioneer IV (extrapolated) and the pre-storm, quiet-day observations for Explorer VI was about 10^3. This last variation should not be regarded as especially significant since it is possible that, although the Geiger counter on Explorer VI detected most of the electrons by their bremsstrahlung, a significant fraction of the electrons detected on the Pioneer IV shot were energetic enough to penetrate the lead shielding so that they could be counted directly with a much higher efficiency (Farley, private communication). Thus the great apparent difference in counting rate may be due to a slight change in particle energy between the times of the two measurements.

The Explorer VI results show that the time variations are very complex and do not fit into any simple pattern. For example, during the early part of the storm of 16 August 1959, Rosen et al. (1960) reported an increase in the outer zone in the counting rate of their plastic scintillator (which detects particles directly with high efficiency and bremsstrahlung with low efficiency) at the same time that Fan et al. (1960) and Arnoldy et al. (1960a) reported a decrease in the counting rate of two Geiger counters and one ionization chamber (which detect Van Allen electrons from their bremsstrahlung).

Three hypotheses have been advanced to account for the existence of the electron belt: (1) direct solar injection, (2) local acceleration within the geomagnetic field, and (3) the decay of neutrons produced by the interaction of galactic and solar-flare cosmic radiation with nuclei of atmospheric nitrogen and oxygen. The first hypothesis is no longer tenable (Dessler and Karplus, 1960; Arnoldy et al., 1960b). Dessler and Karplus raised four independent objections to the concept of direct solar injection; these arguments, none of which have been refuted, may be applied with equal force against the local-acceleration hypothesis. The neutron-origin hypothesis has also been seriously questioned by Kellogg (1960). Dessler and Karplus (1960) have proposed neutron decay as a satisfactory source for the entire electron belt, while Hess (1960) has proposed neutron decay as the source of those electrons with energies above 100 kev. Local acceleration for the outer part of the electron belt has been proposed by Arnoldy et al. (1960a), Singer (1959), Van Allen (1959), and Vernov et al. (1959), and specific local acceleration mechanisms have been put forth by Gold (1959), Herlofson (1960), and Kellogg (1959). However, there has been no general acceptance of any of these mechanisms and the origin of the electron belt remains a controversial issue.

3.2.3. Electron-Flux Measurements

A major uncertainty exists in the value of the flux of electrons in the electron belt. The experiments which determine electron flux may be divided into three types: (1) energy-flux measurements, (2) spectrum measurements, and (3) bremsstrahlung experiments. The least accurate of these measurements are those which rely on the bremsstrahlung process. The most accurate experiments are those which utilize spectrometers, such as the magnetic spectrometer employed near the bottom of the radiation belt by Walt *et al.* (1960) to obtain a direct measurement of the electron flux as a function of energy. However, there have been no spectrometer flights out through the heart of either of the two zones of the radiation belt.

At the present time, the measurements of the electron-energy flux (Vernov *et al.*, 1959a) probably represent the best evidence available from which to estimate the flux of electrons in the electron belt. A value of 2×10^{11} ev/cm²-sec-ster was obtained for the actual energy flux of all electrons with energies between 50 and 1000 kev. This energy flux was measured with a scintillation crystal which was 0.3 g/cm² thick and covered with 1.9×10^{-3} g/cm² aluminum foil. The substance of which the crystal was composed is not stated. (The same vehicle also carried a much larger sodium iodide crystal scintillation counter.)

Transforming an energy flux to an electron flux requires that the electron-energy spectrum be known. The only measurements of the electron spectrum now available are those from the Atlas pod experiment in the inner zone of the radiation belt (Holly and Johnson, 1960), the Javelin I flight into the base of the outer zone (Walt *et al.*, 1960), and the Mechta I and II experiments (Vernov and Chudakov, 1960). The results of the outer-zone Javelin electron-differential-energy spectrum* measurements are shown in **Fig. 3-3** (Walt *et al.*, 1960; Cladis, private communication). This curve differs from the one originally published by Walt *et al.* in that it has been corrected for scattering of electrons within the instrument. The electrons measured in this experiment are not truly trapped in the geomagnetic field but have just been scattered down out of the radiation belt and will soon be absorbed in the atmosphere near the Capetown anomaly (Cladis and Dessler, 1961), an anomalously weak region of the Earth's magnetic field near the southern tip of Africa. Not shown in the figure is a 1-Mev point, which is less than 0.3 electron/cm²-sec-ster-kev and which may be considered to be zero within experimental error. The Atlas pod

---

* The differential-energy spectrum is the distribution as a function of energy of the particle flux within an incremental energy interval. The integral spectrum is the distribution of particle flux with energies greater than a given energy as a function of energy.

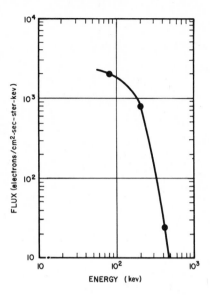

experiments on the inner-zone electron spectrum yielded a spectrum qualitatively similar to this outer-zone spectrum. The Mechta I and II results appear to be in rough agreement with **Fig. 3-3** in the range 100 to 500 kev. For this discussion, let us assume that the shape of the outer-zone electron spectrum is represented by the Javelin I results shown in **Fig. 3-3**, even though this spectrum was obtained with a nonequilibrium electron distribution; it is probably somewhat softer than the equilibrium spectrum that prevails at higher altitudes.

If we assume a spectral distribution such as that given by the Javelin I results, we find that the observed energy flux of 2×10^{11} ev/cm²-sec-ster can be produced by an electron flux of about 2×10^6 electrons/cm²-sec-ster with energies greater than 50 kev. This value corresponds to an omnidirectional flux of 3×10^7 electrons/cm²-sec above 50 kev. Extrapolating the almost flat spectrum down to 20 kev, one obtains an omnidirectional flux of about 10^8 electrons/cm²-sec above 20 kev for the quiet-day electron flux. It has been argued that a flux value of about 10^8 electrons/cm²-sec above 20 kev is consistent with nearly all the space-probe and satellite experiments that have been performed thus far (Dessler, 1960).

The value chosen for the electron flux in the heart of the inner zone (about 3×10^3-km altitude) is 3×10^6 electrons/cm²-sec above 20 kev. This value is in agreement with the flux calculated from the neutron-decay source in the inner zone (Hess, 1960; Kellogg, 1960). The only quantitative theory which has thus far been proposed to explain the origin of these electrons is the neutron-decay theory.

A definitive measure of the electron flux in the inner and outer zones must await measurements of the electron spectrum. As pointed out by Hess (1960), "Making [a] quantitative deduction from a phenomenon caused by an unknown number of unidentified particles of uncertain energies is a questionable procedure." Until spectral measurements are made, the flux values given in this report, in the author's opinion, represent values in agreement with the most reliable experiments and theory.

3.2.4. Spatial Distribution of Proton Flux

The values of proton flux are much better known than those of electron flux; future experiments are not expected to lead to any order-of-magnitude changes in the flux values given here. Contours of proton flux are shown in **Fig. 3-4**. The proton-integral-energy spectrum shows an $E^{-0.8}$ dependence above about 40 Mev (Freden and White, 1960). The outermost proton-flux contour delimits the region generally referred to as the inner zone of a radiation belt; the remainder of the belt is often called the outer zone. The proton-flux contours are symmetrical about the integral-invariant equator. Since the geomagnetic field is not centered about the Earth's spin axis, the heights of the contours above the Earth's surface are a function of longitude. The contours closer than

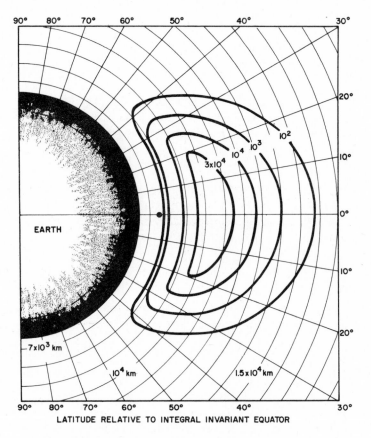

LATITUDE RELATIVE TO INTEGRAL INVARIANT EQUATOR

FIG. 3-4. Proton belt (inner zone) of the Van Allen radiation. The numbers identify flux contours of protons with energies greater than 40 Mev in protons/cm²-sec. The dot at the lower edge of the belt is to be put at the altitudes indicated in Fig. 3-5b to take into account the variations in the altitude and latitude of the belt as a function of longitude. As shown, the altitude of the belt is appropriate for 210° E longitude.

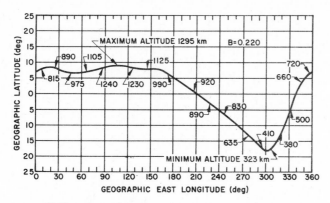

a. Field strength of 0.220 gauss. The numbers are the altitudes in kilometers where the proton flux is barely detectable above cosmic-ray background.

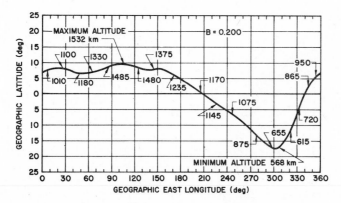

b. Field strength of 0.200 gauss. The numbers are the altitudes in kilometers where the flux is 10^2 protons/cm²-sec above 40 Mev.

Fig. 3-5. Location and altitude of the integral-invariant equator with respect to geographic coordinates. Altitudes shown should be correct to within ±25 km.

1×10^4 km from the Earth's center are probably correct within a factor of 2; beyond 1×10^4 km they may be in error by as much as a factor of 10.

The location of the integral-invariant equator relative to geographic coordinates is shown in **Fig. 3-5**. Altitudes of the base of the radiation belt at various positions around the integral-invariant equator are expressed in kilometers by the numbers at the arrows in **Fig. 3-5a**. The location of the integral-invariant equator and the altitudes were obtained from the high-order spherical harmonic analysis of the geomagnetic field carried out by Jensen *et al.* (1960). **Figure 3-5a** indicates the altitude at the bottom of the radiation belt, where the counting rate is just above cosmic-ray background. The field strength here is $B = 0.220$ gauss (Yoshida *et al.*, 1960). Similarly, **Fig. 3-5b** indicates the altitudes along the integral-invariant equator where the flux of protons with energies greater than 40 Mev is 100 protons/cm²-sec (about 50 times cosmic-ray background). The field strength here is 0.200 gauss.

Figure 3-6 shows the increase in the proton flux as a function of altitude above the bottom of the radiation belt at the integral-invariant equator. This figure was drawn utilizing the data presented by Yoshida *et al.* (1960) and the spherical harmonic analysis of Jensen *et al.* (1960). The bottom of the radiation belt can be located with the aid of **Fig. 3-5a**. The proton flux at a given altitude and longitude along the integral-invariant equator can be found by using **Fig.**

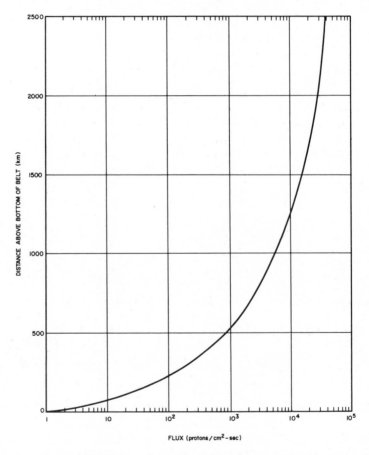

Fɪɢ. 3-6. Distribution of protons, with energies greater than 40 Mev, above the bottom of the radiation belt near the integral-invariant equator. To obtain the altitude at which a given flux occurs at a given longitude, add the altitude indicated here to that shown in Fig. 3-5a. Flux values shown on this graph should be correct to within a factor of 2.

3-5a and 3-6. As an example, let us find the proton flux at an altitude of 1500 km at 45° E. From **Fig. 3-5a** we find that at 45° E the bottom of the radiation belt is 975 km above the Earth's surface. Then from **Fig. 3-6** we see that, at $1500 - 975 = 525$ km above the bottom of the radiation belt (or 1500 km above the Earth's surface at 45°E), the proton flux is 1.0×10^3 protons/cm²-sec.

3.2.5. Spatial Distribution of Electron Flux

The electron-belt contours are shown in **Fig. 3-7**. These contours represent the quiet-day flux of electrons with energies greater than 20 kev. As previously stated, there is a major uncertainty in the values of the electron flux. The flux values given in this figure are generally lower than those given by other authors; however, these contours are based on what, in the opinion of the author, are the most accurate electron-flux measurements and the most acceptable theory. However, if more conventional values for the electron belt are desired, the given flux values should be multiplied by 10^2 for the outer zone and 10^4 for the inner zone as a reasonable upper limit for the quiet-day electron flux which would be consistent with most of the interpretations of the experiments related to the Van Allen radiation belt (*e.g.*, Van Allen, 1959). On the other hand,

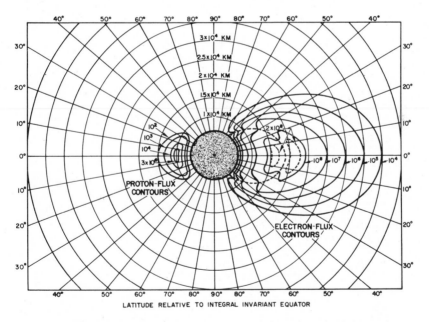

FIG. 3-7. Quiet-day flux contours of electrons with energies greater than 20 kev, in electrons/cm²-sec (proton-flux contours shown for reference). Electron contours may be in error by several orders of magnitude; given electron flux values can be multiplied by 10^2 in the outer zone and by 10^4 in the inner zone to obtain an upper limit, or divided by 10 to obtain a lower limit.

there is evidence that the flux in the outer zone may be lower than shown in Fig. 3-7 by a factor of 10 (Gringauz *et al.*, 1960).

The electrons which are lost from the radiation belt by absorption in the Earth's upper atmosphere emit bremsstrahlung radiation. The shape of the X-ray spectrum due to the atmospheric absorption of Van Allen belt electrons near the Capetown anomaly has been calculated by Cladis and Dessler (1961). Their results are shown in **Fig. 3-8.**

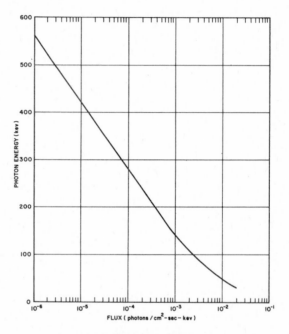

FIG. 3-8. Calculated X-ray differential-energy spectrum from absorption of Van Allen radiation-belt electrons. The magnitude of the X-ray flux is very uncertain—the X-ray intensity will undoubtedly show great time variation and dependence on geographic position. Values given may be regarded as typical for a period of mild magnetic disturbance.

3.3. SOLAR-FLARE RADIATION

After the Van Allen radiation belt, the next most important known penetrating radiation is that from the few solar flares which eject high-energy protons and electrons. Half an hour or more following the appearance of some large solar flares, protons with energies typically up to 200 Mev (Anderson *et al.*, 1959; Rothwell and McIlwain, 1959; Freier *et al.*, 1959) and possibly electrons with energies up to 100 Mev (Freier and Ney, private communication) are detected at the Earth, usually in the polar regions inside the auroral zones. This radiation dies away with a time constant of one to three days. The solar-flare-proton events may be divided into two classes—those which contain relativistic protons and those which contain only nonrelativistic protons. As a working definition, relativistic events are those which are observable at sea level with appropriate instruments, *i.e.,* those events with proton energies greater than 1 Bev. The protons in the nonrelativistic events are all stopped high in the Earth's atmosphere and produce no detectable radiation at the Earth's surface. There appears to be a gradual transition between the relativistic and the nonrelativistic events. No particular significance should be placed on the 1-Bev dividing point chosen here.

During the past 23 years, nine large relativistic solar-flare events have occurred (McCracken and Palmeira, 1960; Simpson, private communication). Equipment capable of observing these events has been in operation since 1937. The largest event was that of February 1956, in which it has been estimated (Meyer *et al.,* 1956) that the flux above 3 Bev was about 3×10^2 times normal cosmic-ray intensity. The occurrence of relativistic events shows no obvious correlation with the solar cycle, although there are hardly enough data to warrant a definite conclusion at the present time. The nine relativistic solar-flare-proton events which have been observed are listed below.

Event	Date	Event	Date
1	February 1942	6	July 1959
2	March 1942	7	May 1960
3	July 1946	8	12 November 1960
4	November 1949	9	15 November 1960
5	February 1956		

The nonrelativistic particle radiation associated with solar flares occurs principally during the years of sunspot maximum. The data for **Fig. 3-9**, which show the number of solar-flare cosmic-ray events per year, have been obtained from experiments which monitor flare-radiation ionospheric effects (Bailey, 1959; Little and Leinbach, 1959; Leinbach, private communication; Hartz, private communication). The events have been divided into two classes—the big events are characterized by maximum fluxes of the order of 10^4 protons/cm²-sec and the small ones by maximum fluxes of about 10^2 protons/cm²-sec.

A model for the solar-flare-proton event may be based on a suggestion made by Parker (1958) and Piddington (1958) that the solar magnetic field is stretched out almost radially inside at least part of a shell of disordered magnetic field which begins outside the Earth's orbit. Solar-flare protons emitted from the appropriate position on the sun may travel directly to the Earth along

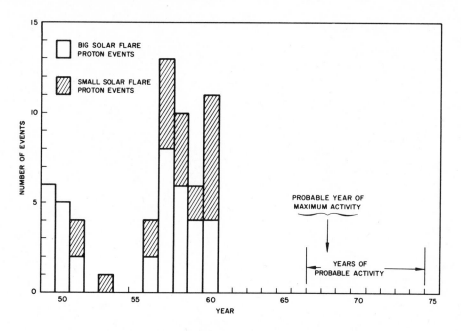

FIG. 3-9. Frequency of solar-flare-proton impingement on the polar cap. The maximum proton flux for big events is of the order of 10^4 protons/cm²-sec, approximately 10^2 protons/cm²-sec for small events.

the nearly radial solar-magnetic-field lines. Protons emitted elsewhere on the sun must reach the Earth by diffusing through the interplanetary magnetic field. This diffusion may be accomplished either by scattering at the disordered magnetic shell and then traveling to the Earth along the radial solar-field lines or by drifting in the radial field because of perpendicular field gradients. An alternate theory (Anderson *et al.,* 1959) requires that, in addition to a radial solar magnetic field, a storage region be provided near the sun from which trapped solar protons are slowly released. Because the protons cannot penetrate rapidly through the disordered magnetic field beyond the Earth's orbit, they are scattered and fill a large portion of the radial-field cavity with an almost isotropic proton flux which has a lifetime of a few days.

The flux values for the flare radiation given in Section 3.6 apply only within the geomagnetic field (*i.e.,* closer than about 6 Earth radii). Beyond the geomagnetic field, the flare radiation could have an intense low-energy component, and it could also have an important electron-flux component. Space-probe experiments thus far have not explored the low-energy component of the flare radiation unperturbed by the geomagnetic field.

3.4. COSMIC RADIATION

Cosmic radiation consists of atomic nuclei moving with velocities near or in the relativistic-velocity range. The composition of cosmic radiation is roughly similar to that of matter in the universe as a whole; that is, the fractional abundances of different elements are about the same in cosmic radiation as in the entire universe. The principal constituent is hydrogen nuclei, or protons, and the next most abundant component is helium nuclei, or alpha particles. The heavy elements are present in somewhat greater abundance in cosmic radiation than in the universe, as deduced from other observations. Further, the elements lithium, beryllium, and boron, which are present in anomalously low concentrations in the universe as a whole, are present in the cosmic radiation observed at balloon altitudes with nearly the abundance which could be expected on the basis of the concentrations of elements which lie next to them in the periodic table. In space, where the Earth's atmosphere cannot modify the primary cosmic-ray nuclear abundance, it may be expected that there will be less difference between the two abundances. The relative concentrations, as given by Peters (1959), are shown in Table 3-1. (Z is the atomic number.)

TABLE 3-1

COMPOSITION OF COSMIC RADIATION

Element	Relative Abundance in Cosmic Radiation at Balloon Altitudes	Relative Abundance in the Universe
Hydrogen	100,000	100,000
Helium	7,000	7,500
Lithium, beryllium, and boron	35	3×10^{-3}
Carbon	190	10
Nitrogen	120	15
Oxygen	190	50
$10 \leqslant Z \leqslant 30$	140	30
$Z \geqslant 30$	<0.1	8×10^{-4}

The cosmic-radiation-proton integral spectrum is shown in **Fig. 3-10** (Barrett *et al.*, 1952; McDonald, 1959). The nearly flat portion of the curve between 10^8 and 10^9 ev indicates that almost no protons have energies in this range, and that their energies lie almost entirely above 10^9 ev. The energy distribution for nuclei other than protons is, in a relative sense, the same as that shown in **Fig. 3-10**; the absolute value for the fluxes of heavier particles must, of course, be corrected for the relative abundances as shown in Table 3-1. (The flux scale should be changed in direct proportion to the relative abundances

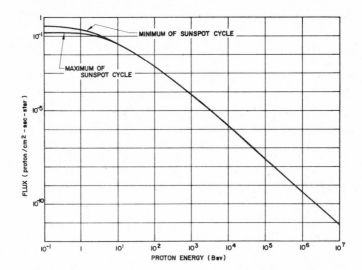

FIG. 3-10. Integral-cosmic-ray energy spectrum at extremes of the sunspot cycle. Space-probe measurements give a flux value of approximately 0.2 particle/cm²-sec-ster above about 40 Mev near sunspot maximum; this value should increase by a factor of about 2.5 near sunspot minimum.

shown in Table 3-1, and the energy scale must be regarded as the energy per nucleon, where the number of nucleons in a nucleus is equal to the atomic weight or the sum of the number of protons and neutrons making up the nucleus.) The velocity distribution is essentially isotropic. The cosmic radiation with energies below about 5 Bev undergoes a variation with sunspot cycle; specifically, the low-energy end of the cosmic-ray spectrum is depleted during sunspot maximum. The change over the sunspot cycle is indicated in **Fig. 3-10**.

The kinetic energy of a particle of rest mass m_0 moving with a velocity v is given by

$$E = m_0 c^2 \left[\frac{1}{(1 - v^2/c^2)^{1/2}} - 1 \right],$$

where c is the velocity of light. When $v \ll c$, this expression reduces to

$$E = \tfrac{1}{2} m_0 v^2.$$

The momentum of the particle is given by

$$p = m_0 v / (1 - v^2/c^2)^{1/2} ,$$

which reduces to the familiar expression $p = m_0 v$ when $v \ll c$.

Since the cosmic-radiation particles are electrically charged, their paths are bent by magnetic fields. The deflection of cosmic-radiation particles by the geomagnetic field prevents the lower-energy particles from reaching the Earth's surface at all, especially at low latitudes. The controlling factor is the ratio of the particle momentum to the particle charge, because the momentum is a measure of the particle's ability to resist change in direction of motion while the deflecting force is proportional to the charge on the particle. It is usual to express the momentum of cosmic-radiation particles in units of Bev/c, where 1 Bev $= 10^9$ ev and c is the velocity of light (1 Bev/$c = 0.53 \times 10^{-13}$ g-cm/sec). The effect of geomagnetic fields in excluding particles from the Earth is shown in **Fig. 3-11** for protons and for alpha particles (Alpher, 1950); the latter are roughly similar in this respect to all the heavier cosmic-radiation particles. Near the geomagnetic equator, protons cannot reach the Earth unless they have momenta greater than about 14 Bev/c. The value depends on the angle at which the particles reach the Earth, and the value given here is for particles arriving vertically. At higher latitudes, particles with lower momenta are able to make their way through the magnetic field, as indicated in **Fig. 3-11**. It is clear that alpha particles (and heavier particles) do not require as much momentum to get through the magnetic field as do protons.

In order to consider the ability of protons and heavier particles to penetrate the magnetic field on the same scale, the rigidity R is utilized—R is the ratio of the momentum to the charge and is defined by the expression

$$R = pc/Ze,$$

where p is the momentum (in units of Bev/c), c is the velocity of light, and Ze is the charge on the particle; R is expressed in volts, which must not be confused with the units of energy, or electron volts. The rigidity is also frequently expressed in billions of volts, or Bv, which is the natural unit to use when the

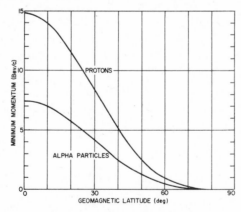

Fig. 3-11. Geomagnetic cut-off momenta for vertically incident protons and alpha particles at the Earth's surface for various geomagnetic latitudes. *Alpher (1959), reproduced with permission of J. Geophys. Research.*

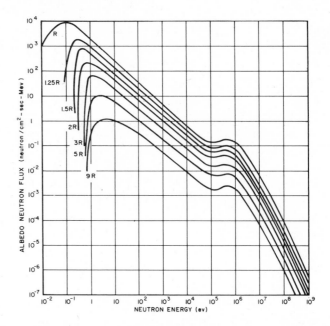

Fɪɢ. 3-12. Spectra of albedo-neutron energy from primary cosmic radiation in space at different distances from the center of the Earth above the geomagnetic equator. The geocentric-distance unit R_e is Earth radii. The $R_e = 1$ curve is for the top of the atmosphere, which for neutrons is approximately 100-km altitude.

momenta are expressed in units of Bev/c rather than ev/c. The rigidity required of any particle to reach any geomagnetic latitude is given by the proton curve in **Fig. 3-11**, where the ordinate scale is regarded as a rigidity scale in units of Bv.

Primary cosmic rays which strike nuclei of atmospheric nitrogen and oxygen produce neutrons, some of which move away from the Earth; these neutrons are commonly called cosmic-ray-albedo neutrons. The albedo-neutron spectrum as calculated by Hess *et al.* (1961) is shown in **Fig. 3-12**. Low-energy neutrons are not present far from the Earth because their lifetime for decay is less than their travel time from the Earth's atmosphere.

3.5. AURORAL RADIATION

Rocket-borne particle-radiation detectors have been flown into auroras (Davis *et al.,* 1960; McIlwain, 1960) and have detected the presence of both energetic protons and electrons. On the basis of surface observations, Ohmholt (1959) has argued that electrons supply the energy for the auroral light. The rocket measurements of Davis and McIlwain confirmed this conclusion. The rocket measurements showed good correlation between positions of high auroral luminosity and high electron flux, and they also showed that the proton flux did not vary over distances of about 40 km even though the auroral luminosity varied greatly over that distance. It was found that both the proton and electron flux were isotropic over the upper hemisphere, and that a negligible particle flux was scattered back in an upward direction.

Both the electron- and proton-energy spectra were found to vary widely from experiment to experiment. The proton-integral-energy spectrum ranged from E^{-4} to E^{-1} above about 100 kev. The flux above 100 kev seemed to lie generally between 10^5 and 10^6 protons/cm²-sec. The electron spectrum in a bright auroral arc was observed to consist of a nearly mono-energetic flux of approximately 2×10^{11} electrons/cm²-sec with energies near 6 kev (McIlwain, 1960). Other rocket observations in a quiescent auroral glow yielded electron-integral-energy spectra which fit power-law distributions above 3 to 5 kev and range from $E^{-2.5}$ to E^{-1}. The flux in these quiescent displays varied between about 10^8 and 10^{10} electrons/cm²-sec. In quiescent displays, the electron flux between 30 ev and 1 kev was always less than 10^{10} electrons/cm²-sec (Davis, 1960).

There appears to be no connection between the aurora and the observed Van Allen radiation. McIlwain (1960) has pointed out that the spectra of auroral electrons and of Van Allen electrons are vastly different. An independent argument may be based on a comparison between the energy required to supply a bright auroral display and the energy stored in the radiation belt. Using the flux values given in this report, the total energy stored in the radiation belt is less than 10^{20} ergs. About 10^{17} ergs/sec are required for a bright aurora. Thus it appears that the entire Van Allen radiation belt would be expended in about 15 minutes in producing a bright aurora. In addition, it is to be noted that the observed radiation belt does not extend to the auroral zones.

A belt of trapped soft radiation which may be connected to the auroral zones has been observed beyond the normal Van Allen radiation belt (Gringauz et al., 1960). A flux of 2×10^8 electrons/cm²-sec with energies greater than 200 ev was measured between 8 and 11 Earth radii. Since this radiation was not detected with other instrumentation flown through this region, the electrons must have had energies less than about 20 kev. The measured flux was 10^3 times too small to account for the particle flux observed in a bright aurora.

3.6. SUMMARY

The various known sources of the penetrating radiations found in space are summarized on the following pages, by type of radiation—*e.g.*, proton radiation and X- and γ-radiation.

RADIATION	FLUX	PARTICLE ENERGY	COMMENTS	REFERENCES
Protons	$(protons/cm^2\text{-}sec)$			
Auroral — altitudes >100 km	Normally 10^4 to 10^6 with $E > 100$ Mev	Integral spectrum, $100 \text{ kev} < E < 800$ kev, varies between E^{-1} and E^{-4}	Good data; flux normally varies by factor of 10, increases in active aurora, decreases during auroral quiet, apparently never stops completely.	Davis et al., 1960; McIlwain, 1960
Van Allen — ±40° from integral-invariant equator, altitudes from 10^3 to 8×10^3 km	Up to $\sim 10^4$	$E^{-0.8}$ integral spectrum above 40 Mev; no radiation observed with $E > 700$ Mev	Fair data; no spectrum observation below 40 Mev; flux increases with altitude (Fig. 3-6) to peak of $\sim 4 \times 10^4/cm^2$-sec at altitude of 3×10^3 km above integral-invariant equator; flux contours, Fig. 3-4; lower edge of proton belt, Fig. 3-5.	Freden and White, 1959, 1960; Hess, 1959; Van Allen, 1959; Fan et al., 1960
Solar-flare — relativistic	Usually 10 to 10^2; occasionally to $\sim 10^4$	$E > 1$ Bev and usually <10 Bev	See Sec. 3.3; usually bombard Earth for less than a day.	Meyer et al., 1956; McCracken and Palmeira, 1960
Solar-flare — nonrelativistic	Usually 10^2 but occasionally to $\sim 10^4$	From 30 to 300 Mev, E^{-1} to E^{-6} integral spectrum; for typical large solar-flare event, max.-intensity integral spectrum might be represented by $3 \times 10^{10} E^{-4}$ protons/cm²-sec, where E is proton energy in Mev; should not be applied below 30 Mev	Fairly reliable data; flux varies over several orders of magnitude, decays roughly as t^{-3}; protons bombard polar cap for 1 to 4 days, produce secondary products (fast electrons and neutrons) by nuclear interaction with Earth's atmosphere; small events observed with Explorer VI; frequency of events, Fig. 3-9; in interplanetary space, flux level may be higher because of lack of shielding by geomagnetic field; low-energy components not yet investigated.	Anderson, 1958; Rothwell and McIlwain, 1959; Anderson et al., 1959; Freier et al., 1960; Fan et al., 1960; Davis, private communication
Cosmic rays — interplanetary space	2 ± 0.3 for $E > 40$ Mev near max. of sunspot cycle; probably increases to ~ 5 near sunspot min.	$E^{-1.5}$ integral spectrum for $E > 10$ Bev	Very good data; flux values measured far from Earth by 3 different space probes agree within 30%; inside geomagnetic field, low-energy component attenuated or missing, should increase near min. of sunspot cycle; spectrum, Fig. 3-10; no sunspot-min. space-probe data; cosmic-ray flux includes heavier nuclei (Table 3-1).	McDonald, 1959; Van Allen and Frank, 1959b; Vernov et al., 1959; Fan et al., 1960; Vernov and Chudakov, 1960
Cosmic-ray ("splash") albedo — <10 Earth radii	~ 1 near top of atmosphere	1 to 10 Mev	No data; flux should fall off as r^{-3}.	Watson, private communication
Electrons	$(electrons/cm^2\text{-}sec)$			
Auroral—from 100 to 1000 km altitudes	Up to 10^{11} to 10^{12}; average $\sim 10^5$ to 10^7	<50 kev; spectrum highly variable; integral spectrum >4 kev between E^{-1} and $E^{-2.5}$; 1 observation showed nearly mono-energetic 6-kev stream	Fair data; flux highly variable (much more so than protons); auroral electron flux and auroral brightness directly related.	McIlwain, 1960; Davis et al., 1960; Anderson and Enemark, 1960
Van Allen radiation	Up to $\sim 10^8$ for $E > 20$ kev	Integral spectrum ranges from E^{-3} to E^{-5}	Fair data on flux, poor data on spectrum; spectrum (Fig. 3-3) probably softer than that of trapped radiation at higher altitudes; flux contours for magnetically quiet day, Fig. 3-7; on disturbed day, counting rate beyond 15×10^3 km may increase by factor of 10 to 10^3, depending on specific instrument.	Van Allen, 1959; Vernov et al., 1959a; Fan et al., 1960; Arnoldy et al., 1960a; Vernov and Chudakov, 1960
Solar-flare—magnetic latitudes > 60°	Probably $<10^2$	~ 100 Mev	Very tentative data; balloon data only; electrons appear late in solar event.	Freier and Ney, private communication
Neutrons	$(neutrons/cm^2\text{-}sec)$			
Cosmic-ray albedo	~ 1	$E^{-0.9}$ differential spectrum for $0.1 \text{ ev} < E < 100$ kev, E^{-2} differential spectrum for $1 \text{ Mev} < E < 1$ Bev	Fair data; differential spectrum, Fig. 3-12.	Hess et al., 1961

REFERENCES / COMMENTS / PHOTON ENERGY / ENERGY FLUX / FLUX / RADIATION

RADIATION	FLUX (photons/cm²-sec)	ENERGY FLUX (erg/cm²-sec)	PHOTON ENERGY	COMMENTS	REFERENCES
X- and γ-Rays					
Electron bremsstrahlung					
Auroral zone	10 to 10^3 above absorbing atmosphere		$\sim E^{-4}$ integral spectrum for $E > 30$ kev	Good data; balloon measurements; flux shows no correlation with auroral or magnetic activity, except X-ray bursts sometimes appear with sudden-commencement-type disturbances.	Anderson, 1958, 1960 Anderson and Enemark, 1960 Brown, private communication
Low-latitude visible aurora	10^3 to 10^5		$E^{-2.5}$ integral spectrum, ~ 100 kev	Measurements not definitive; balloon data: X-rays occur in bursts closely associated with bright visual auroral displays at latitudes below normal auroral zone.	Anderson and Enemark, 1960 Winckler et al., 1959
Atmosphere below radiation belt near 100 km, usually between magnetic latitudes 50 and 60°	$\sim 10^4$		10 to 500 kev; theoretical spectrum, Fig. 3-9	Fragmentary data; magnetic storms cause heating of atmosphere and loss of Van Allen electrons because of increased atmospheric scale heights; this loss of radiation occurs principally beneath tips of outer zone.	Brown, 1959 Rothwell and McIlwain, 1960 Cladis and Dessler, 1961
Van Allen belt		10^{-7}	20 to 50 kev	Only one observation; attributed to electron collisions with residual atmosphere at altitudes greater than 2000 km.	Friedman, 1959a
Nuclear γ-rays from atmosphere above polar caps	$\sim 10^3$ initially		$E > 100$ kev	Data not definitive; observations from balloons; γ-ray intensity closely follows solar-flare-proton intensity; bombardment of atmosphere by solar-flare protons results in emission of nuclear γ-rays.	Brown and D'Arcy, private communication
Solar flares					
Above 100 km on sunlit hemisphere		10^{-2} to 10^{-5}	5 to 80 kev	Good data; output from solar flares highly variable; flux lasts 10 min; weak flux for $E > 10$ kev.	Chubb et al., 1960 Friedman, 1959b
		10^{-4}	~ 500 kev	Theoretical extrapolation from 1 observation, of < 18-sec duration.	Peterson and Winckler, 1959

REFERENCES

Alfvén, H., 1950, *Cosmical Electrodynamics,* Chapter II, Oxford University Press (Clarendon), Oxford.

Alpher, R. A., 1950, "Theoretical Geomagnetic Effects in Cosmic Radiation," *J. Geophys. Research,* **55**, 437–471.

Anderson, K. A., 1958, "Soft Radiation Events at High Altitude During the Magnetic Storm of Aug. 29–30, 1957," *Phys. Rev.,* **111**, 1397–1405.

Anderson, K. A., R. Arnoldy, R. Hoffman, L. Peterson, and J. R. Winckler, 1959, "Observation of Low-Energy Solar Cosmic Rays from the Flare of 22 August 1958," *J. Geophys. Research,* **64**, 1133–1147.

Anderson, K. A., 1960, "Balloon Observations of X-rays in the Auroral Zone I," *J. Geophys. Research,* **65**, 551–564.

Anderson, K. A., and D. C. Enemark, 1960, "Balloon Observations of X-rays in the Auroral Zone II," *J. Geophys. Research,* **65**, 3521–3538.

Arnoldy, R. L., R. A. Hoffman, and J. R. Winckler, 1960a, "Observations of the Van Allen Radiation Regions During August and September, 1959, Part I," *J. Geophys. Research,* **65**, 1361–1376.

Arnoldy, R. L., R. A. Hoffman, and J. R. Winckler, 1960b, "Solar Cosmic Rays and Soft Radiation Observed at 5,000,000 Kilometers from the Earth," *J. Geophys. Research,* **65**, 3004–3007.

Bailey, D. K., 1959, "Abnormal Ionization in the Lower Ionosphere Associated with Cosmic Ray Flux Enhancement," *Proc. I.R.E.,* **47**, 255–266.

Barrett, P. H., L. M. Bollinger, G. Cocconi, Y. Eisenberg, K. Greisen, 1952, "Interpretations of Cosmic Ray Measurements Far Underground," *Rev. Modern Phys.,* **24**, 133–178.

Brown, R. R., 1959, "Excess Radiation at the Pfotzer Maximum During Geophysical Disturbances," *J. Geophys. Research,* **64**, 323–329.

Chubb, T. A., H. Friedman, and R. W. Kreplin, 1960, "Measurements Made of High-Energy X-Rays Accompanying Three Class 2⁺ Solar Flares, "*J. Geophys. Research,* **65**, 1831–1832.

Cladis, J. B., and A. J. Dessler, 1961, "X-Rays from Van Allen Belt Electrons," *J. Geophys. Research,* **66**, 343–350.

Davis, L. R., O. E. Berg, and L. H. Meredith, 1960, "Direct Measurements of Particle Fluxes in and Near Auroras," *Space Research,* ed. H. Kallmann Bijl, North-Holland Publishing Co., Amsterdam, pp. 721–735.

Dessler, A. J., 1960, "Discussion of Paper by R. L. Arnoldy, R. A. Hoffman, and J. R. Winckler, 'Observations of the Van Allen Radiation Regions During August and September, 1959, Part I,' " *J. Geophys. Research,* **65**, 3487–3490.

Dessler, A. J., and R. Karplus, 1960, "Some Properties of the Van Allen Radiation," *Phys. Rev. Letters,* **4**, 271–274.

Fan, C. Y., P. Meyer, and J. A. Simpson, 1960, "Trapped and Cosmic Radiation Measurements from Explorer VI," *Space Research,* ed. H. Kallmann Bijl, North-Holland Publishing Co., Amsterdam, pp. 951–966.

Freden, S. C., and R. S. White, 1959, "Protons in the Earth's Magnetic Field," *Phys. Rev. Letters,* **3**, 9–11.

Freden, S. C., and R. S. White, 1960, "Particle Fluxes in the Inner Radiation Belt," *J. Geophys. Research,* **65**, 1377–1383.

Freier, P. S., E. P. Ney, and J. R. Winckler, 1959, "Balloon Observations of Solar Cosmic Rays on March 26, 1958," *J. Geophys. Research,* **64**, 685–688.

Friedman, H., 1959a, "Round Table Discussion," Chairman L. Spitzer, Jr., *J. Geophys. Research,* **64**, 1799–1800.

Friedman, H., 1959b, "Rocket Observations of the Ionosphere," *Proc. I.R.E.,* **47**, 272–280.

Gold, T., 1959, "Origin of the Radiation Near the Earth Discovered by Means of Satellites," *Nature,* **183,** 355–358.

Gringauz, K. I., V. G. Kurt, V. I. Moroz, and I. S. Shklovskii, 1960, "The Ionized Gas and Fast Electrons in the Vicinity of the Earth and in Interplanetary Space," *Doklady Akad. Nauk,* **132,** 1062–1065 (translation in *Physics Express,* Oct. 1960, pp. 6–9).

Herlofson, N., 1960, "Diffusion of Particles in the Earth's Radiation Belts," *Phys. Rev. Letters,* **5,** 414–416.

Hess, W. N., 1959, "Van Allen Belt Protons from Cosmic Ray Neutron Leakage," *Phys. Rev. Letters,* **3,** 11–13.

Hess, W. N., 1960, "The Radiation Belt Produced by Neutrons Leaking Out of the Atmosphere of the Earth," *J. Geophys. Research,* **65,** 3107–3115.

Hess, W. N., E. H. Canfield, and R. E. Lingenfelter, 1961, "Cosmic Ray Neutron Demography," *J. Geophys. Research,* **66,** 665–677.

Holly, F. E., and R. G. Johnson, 1960, "Measurement of Radiation in the Lower Van Allen Belt," *J. Geophys. Research,* **65,** 771–772.

Jensen, D. C., R. W. Murray, and J. A. Welch, Jr., 1960, "Tables of Adiabatic Invariants for the Geomagnetic Field 1955.0," AFSWC-TN-60-8, Air Force Special Weapons Center, Kirtland Air Force Base, New Mexico.

Kellogg, P. J., 1959, "Van Allen Radiation of Solar Origin," *Nature,* **183,** 1295–1297.

Kellogg, P. J., 1960, "Electrons of the Van Allen Radiation," *J. Geophys. Research,* **65,** 2673–2683.

Little, C. G., and H. Leinbach, 1959, "The Riometer—A Device for the Continuous Measurement of Ionospheric Absorption," *Proc. I.R.E.,* **47,** 315–320.

McCracken, K. G., and R. A. R. Palmeira, 1960, "Comparison of Solar Cosmic Rays Injection Including July 17, 1959, and May 4, 1960," *J. Geophys. Research,* **65,** 2673–2683.

McDonald, F. B., 1959, "Primary Cosmic-Ray Intensity Near Solar Maximum," *Phys. Rev.,* **116,** 462–463.

McIlwain, C. E., 1959, "Results from Explorer IV," presented at NASA seminar on Van Allen Radiation, March 26–27 (unpublished).

McIlwain, C. E., 1960, "Direct Measurement of Particles Producing Visible Auroras," *J. Geophys. Research,* **65,** 2727–2747.

Meyer, P., E. N. Parker, and J. A. Simpson, 1956, "Solar Cosmic Rays of February, 1956 and Their Propagation Through Interplanetary Space," *Phys. Rev.,* **104,** 768–783.

Neher, H. V., 1956, "Low Energy Primary Cosmic Ray Particles in 1954," *Phys. Rev.,* **103,** 228–236.

Northrup, T. G., and E. Teller, 1960, "Stability of the Adiabatic Motion of Charged Particles in the Earth's Field," *Phys. Rev.,* **117,** 215–225.

Ohmholt, A., 1959, "Studies on the Excitation of Aurora Borealis, I, The Hydrogen Lines," *Geophys. Publikasjoner,* **20,** 1–40.

Parker, E. N., 1958, "Plasma Instability in the Interplanetary Magnetic Field," *The Plasma in a Magnetic Field,* ed. R. K. M. Landshoff, Stanford University Press, Stanford, Calif., pp. 77–84.

Peters, B., 1959, "Progress in Cosmic Ray Research since 1947," *J. Geophys. Research,* **64,** 155–173.

Peterson, L. E., and J. R. Winckler, 1959, "Gamma-Ray Burst from a Solar Flare," *J. Geophys. Research,* **64,** 697–707.

Piddington, J. H., 1958, "Interplanetary Magnetic Field and Its Control of Cosmic Ray Variations," *Phys. Rev.,* **112,** 589–596.

Rosen, A., T. A. Farley, and C. P. Sonett, 1960, "Soft Radiation Measurements on Explorer VI Earth Satellite," *Space Research,* ed. H. Kallmann Bijl, North-Holland Publishing Co., Amsterdam, pp. 938–950.

Rothwell, P., and C. E. McIlwain, 1959, "Satellite Observations of Solar Cosmic Rays," *Nature,* **184,** 138–140.

Rothwell, P., and C. E. McIlwain, 1960, "Magnetic Storms and the Van Allen Radiation Belts; Observations from Satellite 1958 Epsilon (Explorer IV)," *J. Geophys. Research,* **65,** 799–806.

Singer, S. F., 1959, "Artificial Modification of the Earth's Radiation Belt," *Advances in Astronautical Sciences,* Vol. IV, New York, Plenum Press, pp. 335–354.

Van Allen, J. A., 1959, "The Geomagnetically Trapped Corpuscular Radiation," *J. Geophys. Research,* **64,** 1683–1689.

Van Allen, J. A., and L. A. Frank, 1959a, "Radiation Around the Earth to a Radial Distance of 107,400 km," *Nature,* **183,** 430–434.

Van Allen, J. A., and L. A. Frank, 1959b, "Radiation Measurements to 658,300 km with Pioneer IV," *Nature,* **184,** 219–224.

Vernov, S. N., A. E. Chudakov, P. V. Vakulov, and Yu. I. Logachev, 1959a, "Study of Terrestrial Corpuscular Radiation and Cosmic Rays During the Flight of a Cosmic Rocket," *Soviet Phys. Doklady,* **4,** 338–342.

Vernov, S. N., N. L. Grigorov, I. P. Ivanenko, A. I. Lebedinskii, V. W. Murzin, and A. E. Chudakov, 1959b, "Possible Mechanism of Production of 'Terrestrial Corpuscular Radiation' Under the Action of Cosmic Rays," *Soviet Phys. Doklady,* **4,** 154–157.

Vernov, S. N., and A. E. Chudakov, 1960, "Terrestrial Corpuscular and Cosmic Rays," *Space Research,* ed. H. Kallmann Bijl, North-Holland Publishing Co., Amsterdam, pp. 751–796.

Walt, M., L. F. Chase, Jr., J. B. Cladis, W. L. Imhof, and D. J. Knecht, 1960, "Energy Spectra and Altitude Dependence of Electrons Trapped in the Earth's Magnetic Field," *Space Research,* ed. H. Kallmann Bijl, North-Holland Publishing Co., Amsterdam, pp. 910–920.

Winckler, J. R., L. Peterson, R. Hoffman, and R. Arnoldy, 1959, "Auroral X-Rays, Cosmic Rays, and Related Phenomena During the Storm of February 10–11, 1958," *J. Geophys. Research,* **64,** 597–610.

Yoshida, S., G. H. Ludwig, and F. A. Van Allen, 1960, "Distribution of Trapped Radiation in the Geomagnetic Field," *J. Geophys. Research,* **65,** 807–813.

4

Solar Radiation

Francis S. Johnson

4. Solar Radiation / *Francis S. Johnson*

4.1. INTRODUCTION

Intense emission of light is the most obvious of all solar features. Visible radiation can be measured at the surface of the Earth. As the Earth's atmosphere absorbs some of the radiation, it is necessary to make corrections for the atmospheric absorption in order to determine the intensity of the sunlight above the Earth's atmosphere. This correction cannot be made for all parts of the solar spectrum, however—there are several bands in the infrared portion of the spectrum to which the atmosphere is so opaque that none of the solar radiation within these bands reaches the Earth's surface, and no measurement can be made. The infrared portion of the solar spectrum is quite regular and smooth, however, and it is possible to interpolate between adjoining spectral regions where measurements can be made. In this way, measurements have been made of the solar spectrum well into the infrared, to wavelengths as long as about 15 microns (μ). Because the wavelengths in different parts of the spectrum are designated in different units, we are stating here these units and their relationships—1 $\mu = 10^{-4}$ cm; 1 A $= 10^{-8}$ cm.

At the short-wavelength end of the solar spectrum, the situation is different; ozone in the Earth's atmosphere, mainly at altitudes near 20 or 30 km, is so opaque to ultraviolet radiation with wavelengths shorter than about 0.3 μ that the solar spectrum observed on Earth is effectively terminated at that wavelength. It would not be possible to say much about this spectral region if it were not for rocket observations made above the atmospheric ozone. At wavelengths shorter than about 0.2 μ, other atmospheric constituents are also opaque and it is necessary to make observations at correspondingly higher altitudes, which rockets can also conveniently reach. In recent years observations have been extended over the entire ultraviolet spectrum down into the X-ray region, although the quantitative values are still tentative and the variation through the solar cycle has not been determined.

4.2. SOLAR-IRRADIANCE DATA

The bulk of the energy in the solar spectrum lies between the wavelength limits 0.3 and $4.0\,\mu$, with approximately 1 per cent of the energy lying beyond each of these limits. This portion of the solar spectrum has been studied at the Earth's surface, with corrections made for atmospheric absorption to obtain the spectral intensity of solar radiation outside the Earth's atmosphere. The distribution of energy in the solar radiation incident on the Earth's upper atmosphere is shown in **Fig. 4-1**, and values of the spectral irradiance (*i.e.*, the incident-energy flux per unit area per unit wavelength) are given in Table 4-1 (Johnson, 1954); these values apply when the Earth is at its mean distance from the sun. The solar constant is the total solar irradiance at the Earth's mean distance from the sun; it is equal to the area under the curve shown in **Fig. 4-1**, and it has the value 0.140 w/cm². The visible and infrared (the ultraviolet not included) portion of the solar spectrum is well approximated in spectral quality by the radiation from a $6000\,°K$ blackbody, whereas the total amount of electromagnetic radiation emitted by the sun is the same as that from a $5800\,°K$ blackbody.

The solar spectrum below $0.3\,\mu$ must be obtained from rocket observations, as virtually none of the solar radiation in this spectral region is able to penetrate the atmosphere and reach the Earth's surface. Below $2000\,A$, or $0.20\,\mu$, the solar-spectral-irradiance curve is well approximated by the radiation which

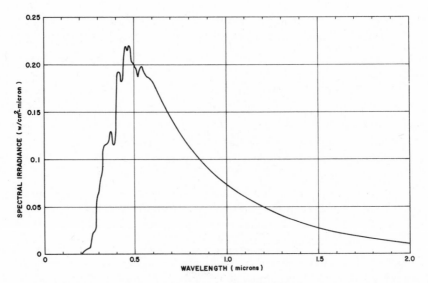

Fɪɢ. 4-1. Solar spectral irradiance above the Earth's atmosphere at the Earth's mean distance from the sun.

TABLE 4-1

SOLAR-SPECTRAL-IRRADIANCE DATA—0.22 TO 7.0 MICRONS

λ[a] (μ)	H_λ (w/cm²μ)	P_λ (%)	λ (μ)	H_λ (w/cm²μ)	P_λ (%)	λ (μ)	H_λ (w/cm²μ)	P_λ (%)	λ (μ)	H_λ (w/cm²μ)	P_λ (%)
0.22	0.0030	0.02	0.395	0.120	3.54	0.57	0.187	33.2	1.9	0.01274	93.02
0.225	0.0042	0.03	0.40	0.154	9.03	0.575	0.187	33.9	2.0	0.01079	93.87
0.23	0.0052	0.05	0.405	0.188	9.65	0.58	0.187	34.5	2.1	0.00917	94.58
0.235	0.0054	0.07	0.41	0.194	10.3	0.585	0.185	35.2	2.2	0.00785	95.20
0.24	0.0058	0.09	0.415	0.192	11.0	0.59	0.184	35.9	2.3	0.00676	95.71
0.245	0.0064	0.11	0.42	0.192	11.7	0.595	0.183	36.5	2.4	0.00585	96.18
0.25	0.0064	0.13	0.425	0.189	12.4	0.60	0.181	37.2	2.5	0.00509	96.57
0.255	0.010	0.16	0.43	0.178	13.0	0.61	0.177	38.4	2.6	0.00445	96.90
0.26	0.013	0.20	0.435	0.182	13.7	0.62	0.174	39.7	2.7	0.00390	97.21
0.265	0.020	0.27	0.44	0.203	14.4	0.63	0.170	40.9	2.8	0.00343	97.47
0.27	0.025	0.34	0.445	0.215	15.1	0.64	0.166	42.1	2.9	0.00303	97.72
0.275	0.022	0.43	0.45	0.220	15.9	0.65	0.162	43.3	3.0	0.00268	97.90
0.28	0.024	0.51	0.455	0.219	16.7	0.66	0.159	44.5	3.1	0.00230	98.08
0.285	0.034	0.62	0.46	0.216	17.5	0.67	0.155	45.6	3.2	0.00214	98.24
0.29	0.052	0.77	0.465	0.215	18.2	0.68	0.151	46.7	3.3	0.00191	98.39
0.295	0.063	0.98	0.47	0.217	19.0	0.69	0.148	47.8	3.4	0.00171	98.52
0.30	0.061	1.23	0.475	0.220	19.8	0.70	0.144	48.8	3.5	0.00153	98.63
0.305	0.067	1.43	0.48	0.216	20.6	0.71	0.141	49.8	3.6	0.00139	98.74
0.31	0.076	1.69	0.485	0.203	21.3	0.72	0.137	50.8	3.7	0.00125	98.83
0.315	0.082	1.97	0.49	0.199	22.0	0.73	0.134	51.8	3.8	0.00114	98.91
0.32	0.085	2.26	0.495	0.204	22.8	0.74	0.130	52.7	3.9	0.00103	98.99
0.325	0.102	2.60	0.50	0.198	23.5	0.75	0.127	53.7	4.0	0.00095	99.05
0.33	0.115	3.02	0.505	0.197	24.2	0.80	0.1127	57.9	4.1	0.00087	99.13
0.335	0.111	3.40	0.51	0.196	24.9	0.85	0.1003	61.7	4.2	0.00080	99.18
0.34	0.111	3.80	0.515	0.189	25.6	0.90	0.895	65.1	4.3	0.00073	99.23
0.345	0.117	4.21	0.52	0.187	26.3	0.95	0.0803	68.1	4.4	0.00067	99.29
0.35	0.118	4.63	0.525	0.192	26.9	1.0	0.0725	70.9	4.5	0.00061	99.33
0.355	0.116	5.04	0.53	0.195	27.6	1.1	0.0606	75.7	4.6	0.00056	99.38
0.36	0.116	5.47	0.535	0.197	28.3	1.2	0.0501	79.6	4.7	0.00051	99.41
0.365	0.129	5.89	0.54	0.198	29.0	1.3	0.0406	82.9	4.8	0.00048	99.45
0.37	0.133	6.36	0.545	0.198	29.8	1.4	0.0328	85.5	4.9	0.00044	99.48
0.375	0.132	6.84	0.55	0.195	30.5	1.5	0.0267	87.6	5.0	0.00042	99.51
0.38	0.123	7.29	0.555	0.192	31.2	1.6	0.0220	89.4	6.0	0.00021	99.74
0.385	0.115	7.72	0.56	0.190	31.8	1.7	0.0182	90.83	7.0	0.00012	99.86
0.39	0.112	8.13	0.565	0.189	32.5	1.8	0.0152	92.03			

Johnson (1954), reproduced with permission of American Meteorological Society.

[a] λ is wavelength ; H_λ is spectral irradiance ; and P_λ is the percentage of the solar constant associated with wavelengths shorter than λ.

would be received from a blackbody source the same size as the sun and having a temperature of 4500 °K (Johnson et al., 1954; Byram et al., 1954). Spectral-irradiance values between 1300 and 2200 A are given in Table 4-2; the values below 2000 A are based on the above-described blackbody source. In addition to this continuum radiation, there are a number of emission lines which contribute only a small amount of energy compared to the continuum above about 1400 A but which contribute the major portion of the solar radiation below 1400 A. A list of the stronger lines which have been observed and their intensities is given in Table 4-3 (Johnson et al., 1958; Hinteregger et al., 1960; Friedman, 1960).

TABLE 4-2

SOLAR-SPECTRAL-IRRADIANCE DATA—1300 TO 2200 A

Wavelength λ (A)	Mean Solar Spectral Irradiance H_λ (w/cm²-A)
1300	5.0×10^{-11}
1400	2.0×10^{-10}
1500	6.7×10^{-10}
1600	7.8×10^{-10}
1700	4.1×10^{-9}
1800	9.1×10^{-9}
1900	1.7×10^{-8}
2000	3.0×10^{-8}
2100	1.0×10^{-7}
2200	3.0×10^{-7}

Solar spectra for the 800 to 2000 A region obtained with rocket spectrographs are shown in **Fig. 4-2** (Detwiler et al., 1960). The NRL values shown here do not agree with the data presented in Tables 4-2 and 4-3—the results are in disagreement with the photon-counter results in the 1300 A region which were weighted heavily in selecting the data for the tables. This disagreement is probably because the different instruments used for the two determinations do not measure the same quantity—the photon counter measures light from the entire sun, while the spectrograph observes a narrow strip across the solar disk. Particularly bright areas on the solar disk show up prominently as bright strips along the spectrum, and these bright areas tend to be the ones which are measured. The photon-counter results can, therefore, be interpreted as indicating that the spectrum shown in **Fig. 4-2** should be lowered by about a factor of 10 in the region 1250 to 1500 A. The intensity shown near 1000 A is supported by data which will be discussed in the next paragraph.

TABLE 4-3

SOLAR-ULTRAVIOLET-SPECTRAL-LINE INTENSITIES

Atom	Wavelength λ (A)	Mean Solar Irradiance (10^{-8} w/cm^2)
Si II	1817	2
Si II	1808	0.7
Al II	1671	0.1
Fe II	1663	0.3
Fe II	1660	0.4
C I	1656–1658	1.8
He II	1640	0.1
C I	1560–1561	0.7
C IV	1550	0.4
C IV	1548	0.5
Si II	1533	0.2
Si II	1527	0.2
Si IV	1403	0.1
Si IV	1394	0.2
C II	1336	0.6
C II	1135	0.5
Si II	1309	0.1
O I	1306	0.4
O I	1305	0.3
O I	1302	0.2
Si II	1265	0.2
Si II	1261	0.1
S II	1260	0.1
N v	1239	0.1
H I	1216	60
Si III	1206	0.1
C III	1175–1176	0.5
N II	1086	0.3
O VI	1038	0.8
O VI	1032	1
H I	1026	2
C III	977	2
H I[a]	<912	1.5
Mg x	625	0.2
O IV	608	0.3
He I	585	0.4
He II	304	3

[a] Lyman continuum.

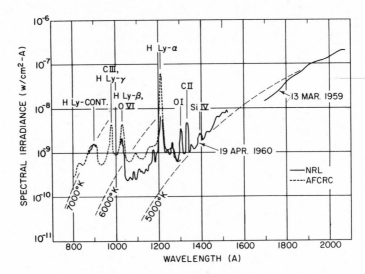

Fɪɢ. 4-2. Solar ultraviolet spectral irradiance above the Earth's atmosphere observed with a photographic spectrograph (NRL) and a photoelectric monochromator (AFCRC). The lines are shown with an effective line width of 10 A. *Reproduced with permission of U.S. Naval Research Laboratory.*

The solar spectrum below 1000 A is shown in **Fig. 4-3**, based on measurements made by Hinteregger *et al.* (1960). Hinteregger's observed intensities near 200 km have been corrected for atmospheric absorption above the observing altitude to obtain the values shown. These **Fig. 4-3** values are not the values presented by Hinteregger, because different corrections were adopted for the absorption above the point of observation. The intensity at 1000 A shown in **Fig. 4-3** agrees well with the NRL value in **Fig. 4-2**. The intensities over the spectral region below 1000 A must still be regarded as tentative; the values shown are probably correct to better than a factor of 5. The spectral lines shown in **Fig. 4-3** are presented with an effective line width of 10 A. Since their true widths are much less than this, their peak intensities are higher than' shown, but the total energies in the lines should be the same as shown.

Below 220 A, the coronal spectrum consists of a dense distribution of spectral lines; it is convenient to consider this as a continuous rather than a line spectrum. Down to 20 A, it can be described as being similar to that of a gray-body emission at 500,000 °K containing a total energy of 10^{-7} w/cm² near the maximum of the sunspot cycle and 1.3×10^{-8} w/cm² near the minimum (Friedman, 1959). **Figure 4-4** shows the distribution typical of the maximum of the sunspot cycle. At shorter wavelengths, the intensity depends a great deal upon the sunspot activity, and sudden changes are observed during solar flares. Typical values for the 8 to 20 A region are 10^{-9} to 2×10^{-8} w/cm², and for the region

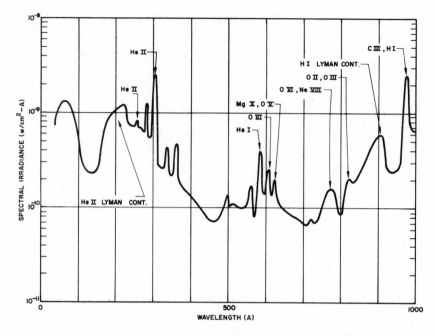

FIG. 4-3. Solar ultraviolet spectral irradiance above the Earth's atmosphere, derived from measurements by Hinteregger *et al.* (1960). The lines are shown with an effective line width of 10 A.

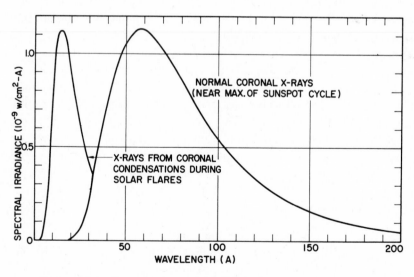

FIG. 4-4. Solar X-ray spectral irradiance above the Earth's atmosphere.

below 8 A, 10^{-13} to 10^{-9} μw/cm². These latter radiations are thought to originate in coronal condensations and the larger values are shown in **Fig. 4-4**. During flares, the shortest observed wavelength is about 1 A, although shorter wavelengths probably occur for a few minutes at the beginning of the flare. On a
few occasions, very short-wavelength emissions have been observed. In rocket
flights, X-rays as short as 0.15 A (or energies as high as 80 kev) have been
observed (Chubb *et al.,* 1960). On a balloon flight, energies as high as 500 kev
(or wavelengths as short as 0.02 A) were observed for a few seconds (Peterson
and Winckler, 1959). However, these are probably very rare and fleeting
events.

4.3. THE SOLAR WIND

Although it is not intended that particle radiation from the sun be discussed
here, the possibility of a continuous outflow of particles from the sun with energies of the order of a kilovolt is probably worth mentioning. This flux of
particles is generally referred to as the solar wind (Parker, 1958). There are
only indirect indications as to the existence of the solar wind, and there are
several divergent viewpoints concerning its strength and persistence. Although
generally considered to be a continuous outflow from the sun, some feel that
the solar wind is intermittent, dropping to zero under quiet solar conditions—
near-absence of flares and other transient phenomena. Still another viewpoint
(Chamberlain, 1960; 1961) is that the velocities for quiet solar conditions are
much lower than the values accepted by Parker, a velocity of about 20 km/sec
being suggested; on this basis, it is suggested that the name "solar breeze" might
be more appropriate than "solar wind."

The most acceptable figures for the solar wind under quiet solar conditions
are probably 10 protons (and electrons) per cubic centimeter at the Earth's
distance from the sun, moving with a velocity of 300 km/sec; protons moving
with this velocity have an energy of 0.5 kev. Under disturbed solar conditions,
the concentrations may rise to 10^2 or higher and the velocities to 1500 km/sec
(10 kev). The enhanced fluxes under disturbed solar conditions give rise to
magnetic storms and auroras. Chamberlain's figure for the velocity is much
lower, and corresponds to a proton energy of only 2 ev.

4.4. SOLAR VARIATIONS

Depending upon one's viewpoint, the sun is characterized by either extreme
constancy or variability. It is an exceedingly stable source of radiation in the
visible and adjoining spectral regions. Any changes which occur in the solar
constant are so small that their existence is difficult to establish. However, even

in the visible emissions, it is clear that the sun is variable, as seen by the appearance of dark spots on the sun, the sunspots. Other indications of variable solar conditions are the prominences which can be seen at the edge of the solar disk with special observing equipment and the structure which can be seen on the surface of the sun when viewed through filters which pass only the light from certain atoms, such as hydrogen alpha (Balmer alpha), or calcium K radiation. Solar flares can be observed by means of such techniques.

The most useful index of solar activity is probably the sunspot number, which exhibits a strong 11-year variation. The sunspot number is obtained by means of an equation involving the number of sunspot groups and the number of identifiable spots. **Figure 4-5** shows the variation in the sunspot number (monthly average values) during the period since the commencement of the present cycle, number 19, in April, 1954 (Lincoln, National Bureau of Standards, private communication). The previous cycle, number 18 (displaced in time to agree with the present cycle), and the average of cycles 8 to 18 are also shown. It is seen that, at this writing, the sunspot activity is about halfway down from the maximum which occurred in 1958. Further, the 1958 period was an unusually intense one, being somewhat greater than twice the average maximum. The minimum is to be expected in 1964 and the next maximum in 1969.

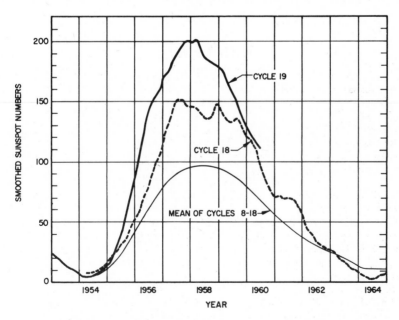

FIG. 4-5. Variation in sunspot number through the solar cycle. Cycle 18 and the mean of cycles 8 through 18 are shown for comparison, displaced in time to agree in phase with cycle 19, which is now in its declining phase. Cycles 18 and 19 were both much more intense than the average of cycles 8 through 18.

During the sunspot maximum, solar flares occur with increased frequency. Some of these generate soft cosmic radiation (see Fig. 3-9), and many of them emit radio noise (see Section 6.5).

The continuum radiation probably does not change perceptibly during the progress of the solar cycle. However, the line radiations from the sun, probably even those at wavelengths as long as 1800 A and particularly those in the X-ray region, must exhibit a strong variation through the sunspot cycle, having a maximum value near the maximum of the sunspot cycle. These are also the radiations which are especially enhanced during solar flares. Different lines change in varying degrees and there is almost no quantitative information on the relative magnitudes of the changes for the various lines. The Lyman-alpha line of hydrogen appears to be one of the more stable emissions; however, it is not emitted uniformly over the solar disk but comes from a number of areas, so that the sun has a patchy or splotchy appearance (Purcell *et al.*, 1960). This property is also characteristic of many of the other lines. These variations have no significant effect on the solar constant, but they are important in connection with the changes they produce in degree of ionization and atmospheric density in the ionosphere.

REFERENCES

Byram, E. T., T. Chubb, and H. Friedman, 1954, "The Study of Extreme Ultraviolet Radiation from the Sun with Rocketborne Photon Counters," *Rocket Exploration of the Upper Atmosphere,* ed. R. L. F. Boyd and M. J. Seaton, Pergamon Press, London, pp. 276–278.

Chamberlain, J. W., 1960, "Interplanetary Gas. II; Expansion of a Model Solar Corona," *Astrophys. J.,* 131, 47–56.

Chamberlain, J. W., 1961, "Interplanetary Gas. III. Hydrodynamic Model of the Corona," *Astrophys. J.,* 133, 675–687.

Chubb, T. A., H. Friedman, and R. W. Kreplin, 1960, "Measurements Made of High-Energy X-Rays Accompanying Three Class 2+ Solar Flares," *J. Geophys. Research,* 65, 1831–1832.

Detwiler, C. R., J. D. Purcell, and R. Tousey, 1960, Paper presented at the Aeronomy Conference, Copenhagen (to be published in *Ann. Géophysique*).

Friedman, H., 1959, "Rocket Observations of the Ionosphere," *Proc. I.R.E.,* 47, 272–280.

Friedman, H., 1960, "Survey of Observations of Solar Ultraviolet and X Rays," *J. Geophys. Research,* 65, 2491.

Hinteregger, H. E., K. R. Damon, L. Heroux, L. A. Hall, 1960, "Telemetering Monochromator Measurements of Solar 304A Radiation and Its Attenuation in the Upper Atmosphere," *Space Research,* ed. H. Kallmann Bijl, North-Holland Publishing Co., Amsterdam, pp. 615–627.

Johnson, F. S., 1954, "The Solar Constant," *J. Meteorol.,* 11, 431–439.

Johnson, F. S., J. D. Purcell, R. Tousey, and N. Wilson, 1954, "The Ultraviolet Spectrum of the Sun," *Rocket Exploration of the Upper Atmosphere,* ed. R. L. F. Boyd and M. J. Seaton, Pergamon Press, London, pp. 279–288.

Johnson, F. S., H. H. Malitson, J. D. Purcell, and R. Tousey, 1958, "Emission Lines in the Extreme Ultraviolet Spectrum of the Sun," *Astrophys. J., ***127,** 80–95.

Parker, E. N., 1958, "Interaction of the Solar Wind with the Geomagnetic Field," *Phys. Fluids, ***1,** 171–187.

Peterson, L. E., and J. R. Winckler, 1959, "Gamma-Ray Burst from a Solar Flare," *J. Geophys. Research, ***64,** 697–707.

Purcell, J. D., D. M. Packer, and R. Tousey, 1960, "Photographing the Sun in Lyman Alpha," *Space Research,* ed. H. Kallmann Bijl, North-Holland Publishing Co., Amsterdam, pp. 594–598.

5

Micrometeorites

J. F. Vedder

5. Micrometeorites / *J. F. Vedder*

5.1. INTRODUCTION

Meteoroids are astronomical bodies which travel in generally large and frequently highly eccentric orbits about the sun. When they strike the Earth's atmosphere, the observable effect produced is known as a meteor. The particle itself is known as a meteorite. Thus, a meteorite is a solid body which constitutes a meteoroid if it is in an astronomical orbit and which produces a meteor when it strikes the Earth's atmosphere. Although a few meteorites are large and weigh many tons, most of them are small. Meteors that can be seen with the naked eye during a few minutes' observation of the night sky are caused by meteorites which are about the size of peas or occasionally even as large as golf balls. Smaller meteorites may produce meteors which can be observed by reflection of radio waves. Meteorites which are too small to produce either visual or radar meteors are called micrometeorites, and their diameters are less than 1 mm.

The existence of dust in interplanetary space has been well established. The dust particles, which range in size down to a few microns ($1\ \mu = 10^{-4}$ cm) in diameter, consist mainly of micrometeorites. Beyond the protective atmosphere of the Earth, meteorites present a possible hazard to space vehicles. The size, mass, spatial distribution, velocities, and number densities of the particles are not well known; however, the data presented in this chapter are considered to be the most reliable estimates presently available.

5.2. RADIATION EFFECTS ON MICROMETEORITES

In addition to the familiar gravitational force of attraction, several other phenomena influence the behavior of micrometeorites in space. On sufficiently small particles, solar-electromagnetic-radiation pressure exerts a repulsive force that exceeds the attractive force of gravitation and sweeps the particles from the solar system. For perfectly absorbing spheres in radiative equilibrium, Robertson (1937) calculates a minimum radius of $0.6/\rho$ micron (where ρ is the density) for particles remaining in interplanetary space without being blown out of the solar system by radiation pressure. The Poynting-Robertson effect (Robertson, 1937; Wyatt and Whipple, 1950), which is a retardation of the orbital motion of particles by the relativistic aberration of the repulsive force of the impinging solar radiation, causes the dust to spiral into the sun in times much shorter than the age of the Earth. The radial velocity varies inversely as the particle size—a 1000-μ-diameter particle near the orbit of Mars would reach the sun in about 60 million years. Whipple (1955) extends the effects to include the solar-corpuscular-radiation pressure, which increases both the minimum particle size and the drag. Further, the corpuscular radiation, *i.e.*, the solar-wind protons, must sputter away the surface atoms of the dust and cause a slow diminution in size, with a resultant increase in both the Poynting-Robertson effect and the ratio of the repulsive force to the gravitational force.

The Poynting-Robertson effect causes the semi-major axis of orbits to diminish more rapidly than the semi-minor axis, with a consequent tendency toward circular orbits as the particles move toward the sun. Also, planetary gravitational attraction increases the dust concentration near the plane of the ecliptic as the sun is approached. At one astronomical unit from the sun (the Earth's distance) the dust orbits are probably nearly circular. If such is the case, the particles within a distance of about 4×10^6 km of the Earth will have, relative to the Earth, a kinetic energy less than their potential energy and they will be captured into orbits about the Earth. De Jager (1955) has calculated the times required for these particles to reach the atmosphere under the influence of the Poynting-Robertson effect, which in this case causes the orbits to become more and more eccentric without changing the semi-major axis. This effect can give rise to a blanket of micrometeorites around the Earth.

Since there is a continual loss of micrometeoritic material in space because of the radiation effects, there must be a continual replenishment; otherwise, micrometeorites would have disappeared from interplanetary space. There are several possible sources. According to Whipple (1955), cometary debris is sufficient to replenish the material spiraling into the sun, maintaining a fairly steady state. Asteroidal collisions are also thought to contribute material. It is also possible that some of the dust in the vicinity of the Earth originated from meteoritic impacts upon the moon.

5.3.   DIRECT MEASUREMENTS OF MICROMETEORITE FLUX

One cannot make a very satisfactory guess about the micrometeorite flux in space. Even in the neighborhood of the Earth, where information has been obtained both directly and indirectly, the derived flux values vary by at least four orders of magnitude. This large discrepancy demonstrates the inadequacies of the experimental methods and the lack of understanding of the various phenomena involved. Beyond a few million kilometers from the Earth, but still in the region of the Earth's orbit, a prediction of the flux of dust is even more unreliable. At greater distances from the sun, the situation is still less certain.

There are several sources of evidence on the micrometeorite environment. Direct information has been obtained from rockets and satellites equipped with impact sensors. In addition, the size distribution obtained from visual and radar observations of meteors may be extrapolated to the micrometeorite domain. From the brightness of the F component of the solar corona and the brightness of the zodiacal light, an estimate of the particle sizes, concentrations, and spatial distribution can be derived for regions of space near the ecliptic plane. Another important source of evidence only recently receiving much attention is the analysis of atmospheric dust for a meteoritic component. The cores of deep-sea sediments and content of collectors in remote regions are valuable in this category. The data provide a measure of the total mass of cosmic material incident upon the Earth.

The direct evidence on the micrometeorite environment near the Earth is obtained from piezoelectric sensors (essentially microphones) and from wire gages; these instruments are installed on rockets, satellites, aud space probes. Statistically, the most significant data have been collected from the sensors on 1958 Alpha (Explorer I), 1958 Delta 2 (Sputnik III), and 1959 Eta (Vanguard III). These vehicles, with large sensitive areas, have collected data for long enough times to give reliable impact rates for the periods of exposure. Many other vehicles with smaller sensitive-area exposure-time products contribute some information.

The impact rate on 1958 Alpha for 153 events was 8.4×10^{-7} impact/cm²-sec for particles of mass greater than 8×10^{-10} g (Dubin, 1960); this mass threshold was derived from the detector calibration and an assumed impact velocity of 30 km/sec. The data show daily and diurnal variations. Ninety per cent of the 153 recorded impacts occurred between midnight and noon, and from day to day the variation of the rate was as much as an order of magnitude. One may conclude that most of the detected micrometeoritic material is concentrated in orbital streams which intersect the Earth's orbit.

There have been contradictory reports from 1958 Delta 2, and the data quoted here are believed to be the more reliable. On May 15, a very large increase occurred with 4 to 11×10^{-4} impact/cm²-sec of mass between 8×10^{-9} g and 2.7×10^{-8} g; for the next two days, the impact rate was 5×10^{-7} impact/cm²-sec; and for the next nine days, the impact rate was less than 10^{-8} impact/cm²-sec (Nazarova, 1960). The data for the first day indicate a meteor stream with a very high concentration of particles and may have led to the high estimates of micrometeorite flux.

Preliminary data from 1959 Eta give an average impact rate of 1.7×10^{-7} impact/cm²-sec for masses larger than 3.3×10^{-9} g for about 1000 events in a 22-day period (LaGow and Alexander, 1960). The day-to-day rate varied by less than a factor of 4.5. The data have not yet been analyzed for diurnal variations. Note that the mass threshold is four times that of 1958 Alpha and that the flux is one fifth as large. If one assumes that the average flux did not change between measurements, a mass-distribution curve is obtained which relates the flux of particles larger than a given radius to the inverse $7/2$ power of the radius.

Space probes have yielded little information. Pioneer I recorded a decrease in flux with distance from the Earth on the basis of 11 counts in 9 hours. With detectors sensitive to three mass intervals and based on a few counts, the second and third Russian space probes indicate that the flux of the smallest particles detected is less than that of larger ones. Being based on so few events, these results are of dubious validity.

The calibration of piezoelectric sensors in terms of the particle parameters is very uncertain. Many workers believe that the response is proportional to the incident momentum of the particles, a relation deduced from laboratory results linearly extrapolated to meteoritic velocities. However, one must expect that vaporization and ejection of material by hypervelocity impacts would cause a deviation from a linear relationship. In the United States, most of the sensors are calibrated by dropping small spheres on their sensitive surfaces. The Russian experimenters claim that only a small fraction of the impulse from the sensors is caused by the incident momentum with the remainder being momentum of ejected material from the sensor. This "ejection" momentum is linearly related to the particle energy. They quote about the same mass threshold as that of the U.S. apparatus, but a momentum threshold about 40 times greater. There is a difference in the experimental arrangement, in that the U.S. microphones are attached directly to the vehicle skin while the Russian instruments are isolated from the skin. The threshold mass is derived from the momentum threshold with the assumption of a mean impact velocity of 30 km/sec in the U.S. work and 40 km/sec in the U.S.S.R. work. The threshold mass of about 10^{-9} g corresponds to a 10-μ-diameter sphere of density 2 g/cm³. However, the conversion from mass to size is unreliable, since many photographic meteors give evidence of a fluffy, loosely bound meteorite structure with densities as low as 0.01 g/cm³. To what extent such low density applies to micrometeorites is unknown. The velocity value used is also open to some question; if a substantial fraction of the dust is orbiting about the Earth, only about one third the above-mentioned average velocity should be used in deriving the mass. Zodiacal light and the *gegenschein* give some evidence for such a dust blanket, a phenomenon also to be expected if the dust before capture is in circular orbits about the sun, as indicated by the trend of the smaller visible meteors. The diurnal variation in the observed flux may be partly due to the dependence of the detector sensitivity on the incident velocity.

The flux of micrometeorites in the neighborhood of the Earth can be estimated by extrapolation from radar and visual meteor data. A summary of meteorite data, prepared by Whipple (1958) on the basis of photographic, visual, and radar evidence, is given in Table 5-1. From an estimated mass of 25 g for a zero-magnitude meteorite, the other masses are derived with the assumption of a mass decrease by a factor of 2.512 for each unit increase in magnitude. The radius is calculated from the mass by assuming spheres of density 0.05 g/cm^3 except for the smallest particles, which must have a higher mass density to remain in the solar system in the presence of solar-radiation pressure. The flux values are for all particles with masses greater than the given mass and are based on an estimate of the numbers of visual meteors. It is assumed that the flux values increase by a factor of 2.512 per magnitude, in accordance with the opinion that the total mass flux in each unit range in magnitude is constant. The values agree with the data from 1958 Alpha and 1959 Eta. The figures in the next-to-last column are derived with the assumption of 50 per cent shielding by the Earth; hence, these figures apply immediately above the Earth's atmosphere. The unshielded flux is given in the last column; these figures constitute the best estimate for the flux in interplanetary space near the Earth. Of course, if there is a dust blanket around the Earth, the fluxes in interplanetary space should be less than the figures given here.

Note that the mass scale is one to two orders of magnitude greater than some previously used; for example, Jacchia (1948) derived a scale of 0.15 g for a 30-km/sec, zero-magnitude meteorite. The older scales were based on theoretical estimates of the conversion efficiency of kinetic energy into light. The mass scale used in Table 5-1 was derived on the assumption that the motion of the glowing trail is related to the momentum transfer to the trail by the meteorite, permitting the calculation of the mass if the velocity is known (Cook and Whipple, 1958).

A concentration distribution has been derived from radar observations sensitive to the fifteenth magnitude (Manning and Eshleman, 1959). Extrapolation of this relationship through the thirtieth magnitude covers the range of micrometeorites. The approximate equation is $n = 1.6 \times 10^{-4}/q$, where n is the number of trails/cm^2-sec with electron line-density greater than or equal to q electrons/cm, and q is proportional to the mass of the meteorite. Therefore,

TABLE 5-1

PARAMETERS OF MICROMETEORITES

Visual Magnitude	Mass (g)	Radius (μ)	Velocity (km/sec)	Kinetic Energy (ergs)	No. Striking 3-m Sphere per Day	Flux (particle/cm²-sec)
0	25.0	49,200	28	1.0×10^{14}		
1	9.95	36,200	28	3.98×10^{13}		
2	3.96	26,600	28	1.58×10^{13}		
3	1.58	19,600	28	6.31×10^{12}		
4	0.628	14,400	28	2.51×10^{12}		
5	0.250	10,600	28	1.00×10^{12}	2.22×10^{-5}	1.83×10^{-15}
6	9.95×10^{-2}	7,800	28	3.98×10^{11}	6.48×10^{-5}	5.34×10^{-15}
7	3.96×10^{-2}	5,740	28	1.58×10^{11}	1.63×10^{-4}	1.34×10^{-14}
8	1.58×10^{-2}	4,220	27	5.87×10^{10}	4.09×10^{-4}	3.36×10^{-14}
9	6.28×10^{-3}	3,110	26	2.17×10^{10}	1.03×10^{-3}	8.49×10^{-14}
10	2.50×10^{-3}	2,290	25	7.97×10^{9}	2.58×10^{-3}	2.12×10^{-13}
11	9.95×10^{-4}	1,680	24	2.93×10^{9}	6.48×10^{-3}	5.34×10^{-13}
12	3.96×10^{-4}	1,240	23	1.07×10^{9}	1.63×10^{-2}	1.34×10^{-12}
13	1.58×10^{-4}	910	22	3.89×10^{8}	4.09×10^{-2}	3.36×10^{-12}
14	6.28×10^{-5}	669	21	1.41×10^{8}	1.03×10^{-1}	8.49×15^{-12}
15	2.50×10^{-5}	492	20	5.10×10^{7}	2.58×10^{-1}	2.12×10^{-11}
16	9.95×10^{-6}	362	19	1.83×10^{7}	6.48×10^{-1}	5.34×10^{-11}
17	3.96×10^{-6}	266	18	6.55×10^{6}	1.63	1.34×10^{-10}
18	1.58×10^{-6}	196	17	2.33×10^{6}	4.09	3.36×10^{-10}
19	6.28×10^{-7}	144	16	8.20×10^{5}	1.03×10	8.49×10^{-10}
20	2.50×10^{-7}	106	15	2.87×10^{5}	2.58×10	2.12×10^{-9}
21	9.95×10^{-8}	78.0	15	1.14×10^{5}	6.48×10	5.34×10^{-9}
22	3.96×10^{-8}	57.4	15	4.55×10^{4}	1.63×10^{2}	1.34×10^{-8}
23	1.58×10^{-8}	39.8[a]	15	1.81×10^{4}	4.09×10^{2}	3.36×10^{-8}
24	6.28×10^{-9}	25.1[a]	15	7.21×10^{3}	1.03×10^{3}	8.49×10^{-8}
25	2.50×10^{-9}	15.8[a]	15	2.87×10^{3}	2.58×10^{3}	2.12×10^{-7}
26	9.95×10^{-10}	10.0[a]	15	1.14×10^{3}	6.48×10^{3}	5.34×10^{-7}
27	3.96×10^{-10}	6.30[a]	15	4.55×10^{2}	1.63×10^{4}	1.34×10^{-6}
28	1.58×10^{-10}	3.98[a]	15	1.81×10^{2}	4.09×10^{4}	3.35×10^{-6}
29	6.28×10^{-11}	2.51[a]	15	7.21×10	1.03×10^{5}	8.49×10^{-6}
30	2.50×10^{-11}	1.58[a]	15	2.87×10	2.58×10^{5}	2.12×10^{-5}
31	9.95×10^{-12}	1.00[a]	15	1.14×10	6.48×10^{5}	5.34×10^{-5}

[a] Maximum radius permitted by solar light pressure.

n is inversely proportional to the radius cubed and in fair agreement with the inverse $7/2$ power derived from 1958 Alpha and 1959 Eta data. At the fifteenth magnitude, $n = 1.6 \times 10^{-12}$ particle/cm²-sec, and at the twenty-fifth magnitude, $n = 1.6 \times 10^{-8}$ particle/cm²-sec. These extrapolated fluxes are about an order of magnitude less than the values from the satellite data and the figures in Whipple's table. The extrapolation may be in error for several reasons. The observational data determining the concentration distribution have a range of error which is magnified in the extension into the micrometeorite region. The solar-electromagnetic- and corpuscular-radiation pressure and the associated Poynting-Robertson effect increase in effectiveness as the particle size decreases and modify the distribution and limit sizes to larger than a few microns. Also, it has been suggested that the source of all or part of the dust may not be the same as that for visual or radar meteorites (Best, 1960), and the same distribution would not be expected.

5.4. INDIRECT INDICATIONS OF MICROMETEORITE FLUX

A measure of the total mass accretion of meteoritic material by the Earth is obtained from analyses of deep-sea sediments and dust collected in remote regions (Pettersson, 1960). Most meteoritic material, by the time it reaches the Earth's surface, has been reduced to dust or to spherules of ablated material in its passage through the atmosphere. For all meteorites, the average nickel content is about 2.5 per cent. This is much higher than the nickel content of terrestrial dusts and sediments and provides a basis for the determination of the meteoritic mass influx. Present data indicate an accretion of about 5×10^6 tons per year over the entire globe, or about 3×10^{-14} g/cm²-sec. If we assume a size distribution as obtained from radar data, we conclude that most of this material arrived above the atmosphere as micrometeorites. The figure agrees well with the total influx derived from satellite data. At the present time, the limited samplings of oceanic sediments and atmospheric dust give only a poor estimate. The average nickel content of meteorites is not well known and may introduce a factor-of-2 error in the results. This technique gives no measure of the size distribution of the primary particles or evidence of short-term temporal variations. The numbers probably are good to within two orders of magnitude.

A method giving more information on micrometeorites is the study of the zodiacal light and the F component of the solar corona. The analysis shows the dust to be concentrated in the plane of the ecliptic and to extend inward to the sun. A particle-size distribution may be derived which indicates that the abundances vary as the inverse 5/2 to 7/2 power of the particle radius. Depending on the assumptions made in the analysis, the absolute values deduced from these observations for the micrometeoritic flux vary by several orders of magnitude with one another. In interplanetary space near the Earth's orbit, Beard (1959) calculates a concentration of 10^{-15} particle/cm³ for a size larger than a few microns. The concentration distribution varies as the inverse 7/2 power of particle radius, and as the inverse 3/2 power of the distance to the sun. The Earth's gravitational field may increase the numbers in the immediate vicinity of the Earth by as much as 10^3 to give a value for the flux at the top of the Earth's atmosphere as high as 10^{-6} particle/cm²-sec, which is in agreement with the satellite data. The data on dust-scattered light are subject to large uncertainties. Beard assumes that the micrometeoritic dust does not polarize the light, although Blackwell (1960) argues that the dust is mainly responsible for the observed polarization. There are several other luminous and scattered-light effects that must be subtracted from the observations to isolate the dust-scattered component. Then the theoretical interpretation and the derivation of size and space distribution and density present calculational difficulties requiring various approximations and assumptions. In Beard's analysis, the capture factor of as much as 1000 is derived from the assumption that interplanetary dust is in circular orbits about the sun and is swept up by the Earth.

Other phenomena are also related to the micrometeorite influx. Study of atmospheric absorption of incoming radiation leads to quite large values for incoming dust (Link, 1955). Bowen (1953) found a correlation between rainfall and meteor showers of some help in predicting the times of higher concentrations of micrometeorites in the vicinity of the Earth. The erosion rate of meteorites (Whipple, 1959) in their journey through space may also give some clue as to the dust concentration.

The four main sources of information still leave one with an uncertainty of about 10^4 in the expected micrometeorite flux near the Earth. Insufficient data, incomplete understanding of the various phenomena, and a real fluctuation in the micrometeorite concentration contribute to this large discrepancy. Beyond approximately 4,000,000 km, which is the capture radius for dust circularly orbiting the sun, knowledge of the particle flux is even less certain, being dependent on the fraction of particles in such orbits and the rates of approach to the Earth. There are probably many unrecorded meteor streams crossing the Earth's orbit that occasionally cause large increases in the dust concentration.

5.5. METEOR SHOWERS

Meteor showers are phenomena which tend to recur on an annual basis. Swarms of meteoroids are orbiting in space, probably roughly in the orbits of old comets. The meteoritic material in most cases seems to be spread around the entire orbit, although somewhat unevenly. If the orbit intersects the Earth's orbit, a meteor shower occurs each time the Earth passes through the orbit of the meteoritic material (*i.e.*, annually). If the meteoritic material is not spread around the entire orbit, but concentrated in one portion of it at any one time, the showers do not occur on an annual basis; a shower will occur at the time the Earth passes through the orbit only if the meteoritic material happens to be in that part of the orbit.

Meteor showers are observed both visually and with radar. When a shower occurs, it is probable that the flux of micrometeorites is also enhanced. As the meteoroids in any one group are moving through space on parallel trajectories, they all appear to come from one point in the sky, known as the radiant. The position of the radiant in the sky can be identified by use of the celestial grid, *i.e.*, by specifying the right ascension and declination.

A list of the meteoroid streams which give rise to meteor showers is given in Table 5-2. Also given in this table are the times at which the showers occur, the positions of the radiants, the meteoroid velocities relative to the Earth, and the maximum rates of occurrence of radio-echo meteors for the more intense known streams (McIntosh, 1935; Weiss, 1960; Whipple and Hawkins, 1959). Many other streams whose orbits do not intersect the Earth's orbit can be expected in space.

TABLE 5-2

METEOR STREAMS

Shower	Date of Maximum	Limits	Radiant R.A. (°)	Dec. (°)	Velocity (km/sec)	Maximum Hourly Radar Echo Rate
Quadrantids	Jan 3	Jan 1–Jan 4	230	+48	42.7	95
Virginids	Mar 13	Mar 5–Mar 21	183	+ 4	30.8	<5
Lyrids	Apr 21	Apr 20–Apr 23	270	+33	48.4	11
η Aquarids	May 4	May 2–May 6	336	+ 0	64	15
Daytime Arietids	June 8	May 29–June 18	44	+23	39	66
Daytime ζ Perseids	June 9	June 1–June 16	62	+23	29	42
Sagittarids	June 11		304	−35		30
Daytime β Taurids	June 30	June 24–July 6	86	+19	32	27
Phoenicids	July 14		32	−48		30
Southern δ Aquarids	July 30	July 21–Aug 15	339	−17	43.0⎰	34
Northern δ Aquarids		July 14–Aug 19	339	− 5	42.3⎱	
Southern ι Aquarids		July 16–Aug. 25	338	−14	35.8	
Northern ι Aquarids		July 16–Aug 25	331	− 5	31.2	
α Capricornids	Aug 1	July 17–Aug 21	309	−10	25.5	10
Perseids	Aug 12	July 29–Aug 17	46	+58	60.4	49
ϰ Cygnids		Aug 19–Aug 22	289	+56	26.6	<5
Draconids	Oct 10	Oct 10	264	+54	23.1	Periodic
Orionids	Oct 22	Oct 18–Oct 26	94	+16	66.5	18
Southern Taurids	Nov 1	Sept. 15–Dec 15	51	+14	30.2⎰	<15
Northern Taurids	Nov 1	Oct 17–Dec 2	52	+21	31.3⎱	
Andromedids	Nov 7	Nov 7	22	+27	21.3	<5
Leonids	Nov 17	Nov 14–Nov 20	152	+22	72.0	<10
Puppids/Velids	Dec 6	Dec 1–Dec 9	140	−50		50
Geminids	Dec 14	Dec 7–Dec 15	113	+32	36.5	80
χ Orionids		Dec 9–Dec 14	87	+21	30.6	
Monocerotids		Dec 13–Dec 15	103	+ 8	44.0	
Ursids	Dec 22	Dec 17–Dec 24	206	+80	35.2	13

REFERENCES

Beard, D. B., 1959, "Interplanetary Dust Distribution," *Astrophys. J.,* **129,** 496–506.

Best, G. T., 1960, "The Accretion of Meteoric Material by the Earth," *Space Research,* ed. H. Kallmann Bijl, North-Holland Publishing Co., Amsterdam, pp. 1023–1032.

Blackwell, D. E., 1960, "Interplanetary Electron Densities" (presented at the American Geophysical Union meeting in Washington, D.C., April).

Bowen, E. G., 1953, "The Influence of Meteoric Dust on Rainfall," *Australian J. Phys.,* **6,** 490–497.

Cook, A. F., and F. L. Whipple, 1958, unpublished (see F. L. Whipple and G. S. Hawkins, 1959, "Meteors," *Handbuch der Physik,* Vol. 52, pp. 519–564; G. S. Hawkins and E. K. L. Upton, 1958, "The Influx Rate of Meteors in the Earth's Atmosphere," *Astrophys. J.,* **128,** 727–735).

de Jager, C., 1955, "The Capture of Zodiacal Dust by the Earth," *Mémoires de la Société Royale des Sciences de Liége,* Vol. 15, pp. 174–182.

Dubin, M., 1960, "IGY Micrometeorite Measurements," *Space Research,* ed. H. Kallmann Bijl, North-Holland Publishing Co., Amsterdam, pp. 1042–1058.

Jacchia, L. G., 1948, "Harvard Coll. Observatory Reprint Ser. II," No. 26 (see F. L. Whipple and G. S. Hawkins, 1959, "Meteors," *Handbuch der Physik,* Vol. 52, pp. 519–564).

LaGow, H. E. and W. M. Alexander, 1960, "Recent Direct Measurements of Cosmic Dust in the Vicinity of the Earth Using Satellites," *Space Research,* ed. H. Kallmann Bijl, North-Holland Publishing Co., Amsterdam, pp. 1033–1041.

Link, F., 1955, "Contribution of Meteoritic Material to the Atmospheric Absorption," *Meteors,* ed. T. R. Kaiser, Pergamon Press, London, pp. 79–80.

Manning, L. A., and V. R. Eshleman, 1959, "Meteors in the Ionosphere," *Proc. I.R.E.,* **47,** 186–199.

McIntosh, R. A., 1935, "An Index to Southern Meteor Showers," *Monthly Notices, Roy. Astron. Soc.,* **95,** 709–718.

Nazarova, T. N., 1960, "The Results of Studies of Meteoritic Dust by Means of Sputnik III and Space Rockets," *Space Research,* ed. H. Kallmann Bijl, North-Holland Publishing Co., Amsterdam, pp. 1059–1062.

Pettersson, Hans, 1960, "Cosmic Spherules and Meteoritic Dust," *Scientific American,* **202,** No. 2, 123–132.

Robertson, H. P., 1937, "Dynamical Effects of Radiation in the Solar System," *Monthly Notices, Roy. Astron. Soc.,* **97,** 423–438.

Weiss, A. A., 1960, "Radio-Echo Observations of Southern Hemisphere Meteor Shower Activity," *Monthly Notices, Roy. Astron. Soc.,* **120,** 387–403.

Whipple, F. L., 1955, "A Comet Model. III. The Zodiacal Light," *Astrophys. J.,* **121,** 750–770.

Whipple, F. L., 1958, "The Meteoritic Risk to Space Vehicles," *Vistas in Astronautics,* ed. M. Alperin and M. Stern, Pergamon Press, London, pp. 115–124.

Whipple, F. L., 1959, "Solid Particles in the Solar System," *J. Geophys. Research,* **64,** 1653–1664.

Whipple, F. L., and G. S. Hawkins, 1959, "Meteors," *Handbuch der Physik,* Vol. 52, pp. 519–564.

Wyatt, S. P., Jr., and F. L. Whipple, 1950, "The Poynting-Robertson Effect on Meteor Orbits," *Astrophys. J.,* **111,** 134–141.

6

Radio Noise

O. K. Garriott

6. Radio Noise / *O. K. Garriott*

6.1. INTRODUCTION

Noise ultimately determines the minimum signal level that any radio receiving system can detect. Without noise, a signal could be amplified indefinitely until the desired output power is achieved. The sources of radio noise which limit the amplification are many and include lightning, electrical power equipment, corona, deliberate man-made transmissions, galactic and thermal radiation, and amplifier noise. Each of these may determine the threshold noise level in some particular portion of the radio spectrum. It is therefore convenient to divide the spectrum roughly into three parts that are determined by the principal noise source in each part.

Below approximately 20 Mc, the minimum noise level is set by atmospheric and man-made generators. Between 20 to 50 Mc and 1000 Mc, cosmic noise limits the ability to detect weak signals, although man-made interference is also important up to several hundred megacycles. Above 1000 Mc, the cosmic background drops to very low intensities and the thermal noise generated in the detection equipment predominates.

6.2. ATMOSPHERIC AND MAN-MADE NOISE

The frequency spectrum below 20 Mc is characterized by very high noise levels, principally due to natural electrical disturbances in the atmosphere, such as lightning. In addition, large contributions to the background noise are made by electrical equipment, power transmission, and corona discharges. Coherent radiation in nearby communication channels frequently provides the greatest source of interference in this frequency range. The noise levels from these sources are all closely related to the variations of electron concentration in the ionosphere.

In the above frequency range, a convenient measure of the noise level is the ratio of the power (P_a) available from a lossless antenna to that of a resistor at some reference temperature, usually about 300 °K. This ratio, expressed in decibels (db), may be defined as

$$F_e = 10 \log \left[P_a / k T_0 (\Delta f) \right],$$

where k is the Boltzmann constant (1.38×10^{-16} ergs/°K), T is the reference temperature ($300\ °K$), and (Δf) is the noise bandwidth. At 10 Mc, nighttime values of F_e equal to 40 or 50 db are typical and they increase even further at lower frequencies. The power available can also be expressed as an equivalent temperature, $T_e = P_a / k (\Delta f)$. Noise levels below 10 Mc therefore correspond to equivalent temperatures well above $16^6\ °K$. This value is considerably in excess of that expected for galactic radiation.

As mentioned above, the ionosphere strongly affects the atmospheric noise level. In the daytime, solar ultraviolet radiation is responsible for the creation of the D and E regions of the ionosphere. Because of the high electron-collision frequency in these regions, the absorption of passing radio waves is relatively large. Since most of the noise energy is propagated around the Earth by reflection between the ground and the ionosphere, this "sky-wave" propagation is heavily attenuated in the daytime. Daytime noise levels are consequently 20 to 30 db below those measured at night.

Interference from communications circuits may be expected to frequencies as high as 50 Mc by day and up to 10 or 15 Mc at night, because the ionosphere will provide long-distance oblique radio reflections at frequencies somewhat greater than three times the F-region critical frequency. Tropospheric and ionospheric scattering may result in the propagation of weak signals at even higher frequencies.

6.3. COSMIC NOISE

The second region of the radio spectrum to be considered is that between 20 and 1000 Mc. Near 20 Mc, the atmospheric noise level falls to about the same value as that of the galactic background. Also, the frequency is now sufficiently high for the incident galactic radiation to penetrate the ionospheric F region, which it could not do at the lower frequencies. Noise levels in equivalent temperature (or brightness temperature) may now be specified for different parts of the sky. It was this very fact which led Karl Jansky (1932) to the discovery of "cosmic static." He noticed a peak in the observed noise levels whose apparent direction at a fixed time each day seemed to change slowly. Extended observation revealed that the direction was fixed when sidereal time rather than solar time was used. The direction of the maximum intensity was then determined to be that of the center of the galaxy. In the last 15 years, much effort has been devoted to mapping the celestial sphere in terms of brightness temperature at various radio frequencies.

At 18.3 Mc, the brightness temperature of the sky is about 300,000 °K in the direction of the galactic center, but only 60,000 °K toward the galactic pole (Shain, 1954). These galactic noise levels decrease with frequency. Many radio surveys have now been completed and a listing of their pertinent parameters has been given by Ko (1958). **Figure 6-1**, plotted in galactic coordinates, shows the 250-Mc survey made by Ko. A comparison of the various surveys reveals the rate at which the brightness temperature decreases with frequency. Shain concluded that the ratio of the temperature at 18.3 Mc to that at 100 Mc is about 120, except near the galactic center. Near the galactic center, the ratio is lower because of partial absorption of the 18.3-Mc radiation, just as visual observations are obscured by dust clouds in this region.

As the galactic temperatures decrease with frequency, considerable difficulty is experienced at the higher frequencies in maintaining the receiver noise at the low level necessary for the determination of the brightness temperature. In the vicinity of a few hundred megacycles, the noise generated in a good low-noise triode makes a contribution to the output level equal to that of an antenna directed toward the galactic background (several hundred degrees). The recent development of parametric amplifiers should reduce the receiver noise contribution to less than 100 °K below 1000 Mc.

6.4. RECEIVER NOISE

The third frequency range to be considered is that above 1000 Mc. At this frequency, the galactic background temperature is generally less than 10 °K, although it approaches 100 °K near the galactic center. The detection of weak galactic radiation and planetary emission is seriously hampered by the thermal noise generated in the receiving equipment. However, the fact that the receiver noise contribution may greatly exceed the temperature of a faint source does not mean that weak radio emitters must go undetected. Techniques have been devised which permit a comparison to be made between the antenna temperature and a reference noise level (Dicke, 1946; Drake and Ewen, 1958). In this way, variations of the antenna temperature on the order of 0.01 °K have been observed.

The various noise contributions are summarized graphically in **Fig. 6-2** (Strum, 1958). Above 1000 Mc, switched receivers based on the Dicke principle are frequently used with traveling-wave tubes. Masers and parametric amplifiers (not illustrated) permit great improvements to be made, although additional factors must be considered when working at the lowest temperatures. Antenna side lobes and attenuation in the transmission lines, for example, may introduce appreciable noise power. The intensity of emissions from galactic

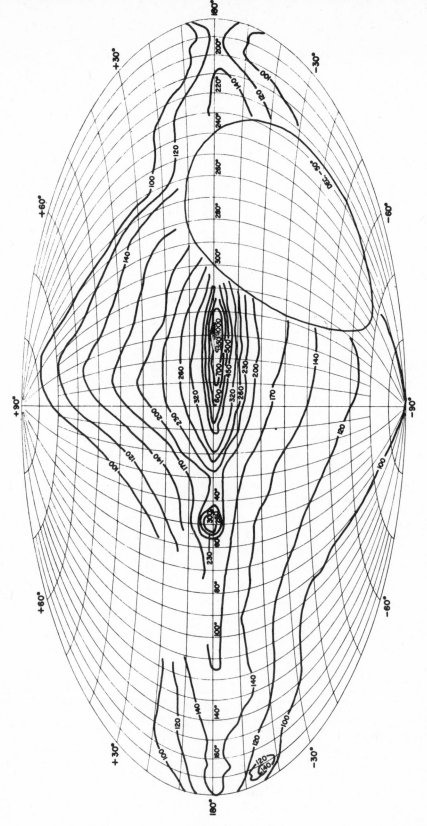

Fig. 6-1. Contours of brightness temperature of the galaxy at 250 Mc. *Ko (1958), reproduced with permission of Institute of Radio Engineers.*

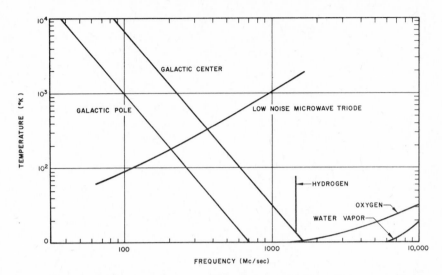

FIG. 6-2. Brightness temperature of the galaxy as a function of frequency. Also shown are the emissions from galactic hydrogen at 21 cm and the emissions from atmospheric oxygen and water vapor. *Strum (1958), reproduced with permission of Institute of Radio Engineers.*

hydrogen and from atmospheric oxygen and water vapor are also shown in **Fig. 6-2.**

6.5.   DISCRETE ASTRONOMICAL SOURCES

In addition to the relatively uniform background radiation from galactic and other sources, there are a large number of discrete sources of radio emission. Initially, it was believed likely that these "point" sources were associated with individual stars of the galaxy. However, as instruments of higher resolving power became available, it became evident that the emission arose over more extended areas. In a number of cases, the radio emissions have been associated with various optical objects and several classes of radio emitters have been found. These include: remnants of supernovae (Crab nebula), galaxies in collision (Cygnus), normal external galaxies (Andromeda) similar to our own, and planets (Jupiter and Saturn). Although the reasons for the galactic radiation are not well established, it appears that synchrotron radiation is the most likely explanation (Burbidge, 1959).

The sun is a very important radio emitter. The background and slowly varying component of the solar radiation is thermal in origin and follows the normal blackbody-radiation law. At frequencies below approximately 1500 Mc, the radiation is generated at a considerable height above the visible photosphere. The observed temperatures are therefore in the vicinity of 10^6 °K, appropriate to the solar corona. At 3-cm wavelengths, the radiation originates at much lower levels, and temperatures between 5000 and 10,000 °K are found. Superimposed on the sun's background are bursts of strong radiation that may last from fractions of a second to several minutes. At frequencies of several hundred megacycles, they have power outputs which exceed the steady emission of the entire quiet sun. The noise bursts have been classified according to their various types, as listed in Table 6-1.

TABLE 6-1

TYPES OF SOLAR-RADIO-NOISE BURSTS

Type	Description
I	Noise storm; short and irregular
II	Slow drift; broad band and slowly falling in frequency (5- to 10-min burst duration)
III	Fast drift; relatively narrow-band bursts falling in frequency (approximately 10-sec duration)
IV	Continuous bursts; broad-band bursts lasting for many minutes; associated with solar flares that frequently eject penetrating high-energy particles (low-energy cosmic radiation) and which often are followed by magnetic storms on Earth about a day after the occurrence of the flare

REFERENCES

Burbidge, G. R., 1959, "The Theoretical Explanation of Radio Emission" (paper No. 98), *Paris Symposium on Radio Astronomy,* ed. R. N. Bracewell, Stanford University Press, Stanford, California, pp. 541–551.

Dicke, R. H., 1946, "The Measurement of Thermal Radiation at Microwave Frequencies," *Rev. Sci. Instr.,* 17, 268–275.

Drake, F. D., and Ewen, H. I., 1958, "A Broad-Band Microwave Source Comparison Radiometer for Advanced Research in Radio Astronomy," *Proc. I.R.E.,* 46, 53–60.

Jansky, K. G., 1932, "Directional Studies of Atmospherics at High Frequencies," *Proc. I.R.E.,* 20, 1920–1932.

Ko, H. C., 1958, "The Distribution of Cosmic Radio Background Radiation," *Proc. I.R.E.,* 46, No. 1, 208–215.

Shain, C. A., 1954, "A Comparison of the Intensities of Cosmic Noise Observed at 18.3 Mc/s and at 100 Mc/s," *Australian J. Phys.,* 7, 150–164.

Strum, P. D., 1958, "Considerations in High-Sensitivity Microwave Radiometry," *Proc. I.R.E.,* 46, 43–53.

7

Thermal Radiation from the Earth

Francis S. Johnson

7. Thermal Radiation from the Earth / *Francis S. Johnson*

7.1. INTRODUCTION

The problem of selecting reasonable values for radiation from the Earth is quite complicated when one is interested in values in several locations at various times. Much of the problem arises because of the complications associated with meteorological phenomena which involve the transport of heat energy. Consequently, for average values of radiation from the Earth, it is desirable to make use of meteorological studies pertaining to the heat balance of the Earth. One of the best of these studies was made by Baur and Philipps (1934, 1935). Tabulated values, principally from their study, will be presented here.

There are two parts to the problem of the Earth's heat balance: first, the relatively short-wavelength solar radiation; and second, the relatively long-wavelength thermal radiation from the Earth, including the atmosphere. Only a portion of the incident solar energy becomes involved in the Earth's heat budget because a substantial portion of the solar radiation is returned to space unused.

7.2. DISTRIBUTION OF SOLAR HEATING

The input of solar energy to the Earth is essentially a geometrical problem; however the solid geometry of the situation is fairly complicated. List (1951) presented values for the average insolation incident on the Earth's atmosphere as a function of latitude and time of year. Values for the Northern Hemisphere are reproduced in Table 7-1. It must be remembered that these are values averaged over a period of a day or longer. To get values for a particular time, it would be necessary to construct the solar-altitude curve for the given latitude and time of year and to use this information to determine the variation throughout the day. Such a curve can be normalized using data from Table 7-1. Alternatively, the knowledge of the solar-altitude angle and the solar constant could be used to obtain instantaneous values for the incident radiation, in which case

TABLE 7-1

AVERAGE INSOLATION INCIDENT ON THE EARTH'S ATMOSPHERE

Latitude (°)	Average Insolation (w/cm²)			
	Jan	21 Mar	Jul	23 Sep
0–10	0.0389	0.0420	0.0408	0.0420
10–20	0.0340	0.0413	0.0438	0.0404
20–30	0.0287	0.0389	0.0441	0.0389
30–40	0.0219	0.0340	0.0441	0.0350
40–50	0.0146	0.0297	0.0441	0.0297
50–60	0.0073	0.0249	0.0441	0.0297
60–90	0.0020	0.0098	0.0462	0.0098

the solar constant must be corrected according to season to take into account the Earth's varying distance from the sun. This latter procedure was followed in preparing the data for Table 7-1, with integration of values over the period of a day to get the time-averaged values presented.

The solar radiation incident upon the Earth's atmosphere is partially absorbed by the atmosphere and the Earth's surface and partially reflected or scattered by the Earth's surface and atmosphere. The portion scattered and reflected back into space is generally referred to as albedo; unfortunately no tabulated values were given for this portion by Baur and Philipps (1934). However, they do give average values for the energy absorbed in the Earth's atmosphere and at the Earth's surface. These data are presented in Table 7-2.

TABLE 7-2

AVERAGE SHORT-WAVE-ENERGY ABSORPTION

Latitude (°)	Energy Absorbed by Atmosphere (w/cm²)				Energy Absorbed by Earth's Surface (w/cm²)			
	Jan	21 Mar	Jul	23 Sep	Jan	21 Mar	Jul	23 Sep
0–10	0.0066	0.0071	0.0077	0.0076	0.0174	0.0193	0.0160	0.0179
10–20	0.0052	0.0062	0.0081	0.0071	0.0165	0.0207	0.0165	0.0168
20–30	0.0039	0.0054	0.0075	0.0060	0.0132	0.0190	0.0205	0.0186
30–40	0.0028	0.0046	0.0069	0.0050	0.0090	0.0158	0.0220	0.0171
40–50	0.0019	0.0038	0.0069	0.0043	0.0052	0.0123	0.0189	0.0130
50–60	0.0009	0.0029	0.0067	0.0036	0.0025	0.0095	0.0168	0.0091
60–90	0.0001	0.0018	0.0078	0.0027	0.0002	0.0047	0.0160	0.0047

The albedo is that portion of the incident radiation that is reflected to space without absorption. Average values for particular latitudes and seasons can be obtained by subtracting the absorbed radiation (Table 7-2) from the incident insolation (Table 7-1). Values determined in this manner are presented in

Table 7-3. As with Table 7-1, the explicit time dependence through the course of the day is not shown or readily available in tabular form. To get these values it would be necessary to make some assumption such as that the intensity of the returned solar radiation is proportional to the intensity of the incident solar radiation. In this case, one would have to determine the curves of solar altitude versus time of day for the region and time of year concerned. The intensity of solar radiation per unit area of Earth's surface would be proportional to the sine of the solar-altitude angle. Curves of sine of solar-altitude angle versus time of day could be normalized so that the areas under the curves agree with the values in Table 7-3; the curves then would represent the time variation of the returned solar radiation through the day, subject to the assumption mentioned above.

TABLE 7-3

AVERAGE SHORT-WAVE SOLAR ENERGY REFLECTED BY THE ATMOSPHERE AND EARTH

Latitude (°)	Short-Wave Energy Reflected (w/cm²)			
	Jan	21 Mar	Jul	23 Sep
0–10	0.0150	0.0156	0.0171	0.0165
10–20	0.0123	0.0144	0.0192	0.0165
20–30	0.0116	0.0145	0.0161	0.0143
30–40	0.0101	0.0136	0.0152	0.0129
40–50	0.0075	0.0136	0.0183	0.0124
50–60	0.0043	0.0125	0.0206	0.0170
60–90	0.0017	0.0033	0.0224	0.0024

7.3.   THERMAL RADIATION FROM THE EARTH

The remaining part of the radiation from the Earth and atmosphere is the long-wavelength radiation. In considering the total radiation emitted by the Earth and atmosphere, it is not necessary to differentiate between that portion of the radiation originating at the Earth's surface and that portion originating within the Earth's atmosphere. Values for the total outgoing radiation are shown in Table 7-4 (Baur and Philipps, 1934). The values have been averaged over a period of a day or longer and, while one would probably prefer to know the time dependence of this quantity throughout the day, the variation between the daytime and nighttime values can perhaps be ignored because it is not great.

All of the tabulated values except those for the solar insolation are apt to be highly variable. For example, water, which covers most of the Earth's surface, absorbs over 90 per cent of the incident solar radiation when the solar-altitude angle is above 25 deg. This absorption would lead to an extremely low albedo

TABLE 7-4

TOTAL LONG-WAVE RADIATION FROM THE EARTH AND ATMOSPHERE

Latitude (°)	Long-Wave Energy Radiated (w/cm²)			
	Jan	21 Mar	Jul	23 Sep
0–10	0.0203	0.0212	0.0209	0.0206
10–20	0.0206	0.0210	0.0210	0.0211
20–30	0.0203	0.0204	0.0213	0.0213
30–40	0.0193	0.0194	0.0216	0.0213
40–50	0.0175	0.0175	0.0202	0.0201
50–60	0.0164	0.0164	0.0195	0.0185
60–90	0.0156	0.0152	0.0189	0.0177

when the sky is very clear, whereas in the presence of extensive cloudiness about half of the incident solar radiation may be reflected, representing a change by a factor of 5 or more from the extreme of no cloudiness. Similarly, in the case of the outgoing radiation from the Earth and atmosphere, one can imagine the extreme of dry and cloudless conditions and of extensive high-level cloudiness. In the former case there will be appreciable radiation from the Earth's surface at temperatures as high as $+30\,°C$; while in the latter, the source of the radiation may have a temperature of as low as $-55\,°C$.

Figure 7-1 shows schematically a typical spectral-radiance (*i.e.,* intensity of emission per unit area per unit wavelength) curve for the radiation emitted by the Earth and its atmosphere. The upper blackbody curve represents radiation from the Earth's surface when the surface temperature is 288 °K. In spectral regions where the atmosphere is transparent, the radiation from the Earth's surface escapes into space. In spectral regions where the Earth's atmosphere is very opaque, the escaping radiation comes from the stratospheric region of the atmosphere, where a temperature of 218 °K is frequently representative (lower blackbody curve). In spectral regions where the atmospheric transparency is intermediate, the radiation to space falls between the two blackbody curves, as illustrated by the solid curve. It must be emphasized that **Fig. 7-1** is only illustrative of the problem, since there are many variables. The temperature of the Earth's surface varies in position and time, so that the 288 °K value suggested in **Fig. 7-1** is only an average. The atmospheric transparency varies a great deal, principally because of varying amounts of water vapor if the air is clear and varying degrees and altitudes of cloudiness if the air is not clear. Although much more detailed and more accurate predictions than those shown in **Fig. 7-1** can be made for specific situations, observational data from satellites will be required before a good overall specification of the Earth's thermal-radiation environment can be given.

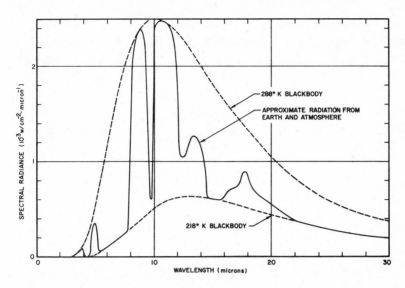

Fig. 7-1. Typical spectral-radiance curve for thermal radiation leaving the Earth. The 288 °K blackbody curve approximates the radiation from the Earth's surface, and the 218 °K blackbody curve approximates the radiation from the atmosphere in those spectral regions where the atmosphere is opaque.

7.4. AIRGLOW

Another type of atmospheric emission is known as the airglow, which is an emission in the visible, ultraviolet, and near-infrared portions of the spectrum. Since such emissions cannot be thermally excited at the temperatures occurring in the atmosphere, some other source of excitation is required. During the day-time and at twilight, absorption of solar radiation is probably the main source. However, the airglow continues through the night. Excited states with lifetimes long enough to account for emission throughout the night do not constitute an adequate explanation. Although the source of the night-airglow excitation is not known, it is probably chemical energy released in the recombination of atomic species into molecules.

The intensity of the night airglow is relatively weak, although it can easily be noted on a clear moonless night by holding one's hand overhead. The area covered by one's hand is clearly darker than the region between the stars; this difference is due to the airglow. Among the prominent emissions from the night sky are those of atomic oxygen at 5577 and 6300 A, sodium at 5893 A, molecular oxygen in the near ultraviolet, and hydroxyl radicals mainly in the near infra-red. The emissions originate principally in the region between 80 and 100 km, where most of the recombination of atoms occurs. A notable exception to this is the oxygen 6300 A radiation, which originates at a considerably higher altitude. It is common practice to express the intensity of the emissions in terms of rayleighs, where 1 rayleigh equals 10^6 photons emitted per second in a square-centimeter column extending up through the atmosphere. The oxygen green line at 5577 A generally falls within a factor of 3 of 200 rayleighs, and the oxygen red line at 6300 A within a factor of 5 of 100 rayleighs. The molecular-oxygen Hertzberg bands in the near ultraviolet amount to about 150 rayleighs, and the hydroxyl-radical emission is about 7×10^6 rayleighs. A recent review of the night airglow has been given by Bates (1960).

REFERENCES

Bates, D. R., 1960, "The Airglow," *Physics of the Upper Atmosphere,* ed. J. A. Ratcliffe, Academic Press, New York, pp. 219–267.

Baur, F., and H. Philipps, 1934, "Der Wärmehaushalt der Lufthülle der Nordhalbkugel in Januar und Juli und zur Zeit der Äquinoktien und Solstitien. Pt. I. Die Einstrahlung bei normaler Solarkonstante," *Gerlands Beitr. Geophys.,* **42,** 160–207.

Baur, F., and H. Philipps, 1935, "Der Wärmeshaushalt der Lufthülle der Nordhalbkugel in Januar und Juli zur Zeit der Äquinoktien und Solstiten. Part II. Ausstrahlung, Gegenstrahlung und meridionder Warmetransport bei normaler Solarkonstante," *Gerlands Beitr. Geophys.,* **45,** 82–132.

List, R. J. (1951), *Smithsonian Meteorological Tables,* 6th edition, Smithsonian Institution, Washington, D.C.

8

Geomagnetism

A. J. Dessler

8. Geomagnetism / *A. J. Dessler*

8.1. INTRODUCTION

The gross features of the geomagnetic field are similar to those of a uniformly magnetized sphere. However, in detail, such a simple model is inadequate. There are many irregularities which cause deviations from a smooth dipole field. Aside from the irregularities, the axis which would represent the axis of magnetization of the Earth does not pass through the Earth's center but is eccentric. In addition, the geomagnetic field varies continuously in an irregular manner.

The Earth's main magnetic field is commonly supposed to originate by dynamo action in the fluid motion of the molten metallic core of the Earth (Elsasser, 1950). This fluid motion is not stable; rather, it changes slightly from year to year and produces the secular variation, which requires hundreds of years to produce a significant change in the geomagnetic field. Transient variations, which take place in times less than one year (some occurring in a small fraction of a second), are produced chiefly by the interaction between solar plasma and the geomagnetic field.

Scientific observations of geomagnetic field have been made for the past several hundred years. For example, the secular variation was discovered in 1635, by means of data obtained as early as 1580. The transient variations were discovered in 1722. The first magnetic observatories were constructed during the late eighteenth century for the purpose of making systematic observations over widely separated geographic positions. Since that time enormous amounts of data have been gathered. An outstanding job of describing, summarizing, and analyzing the data to 1940 may be found in *Geomagnetism* by Chapman and Bartels (1940).

Research since 1940 has been directed mainly toward an understanding of the transient variations. The greatest progress in this direction has come about through applications of the principles of hydromagnetism. In an early paper based on these principles, Parker (1956) pointed out that, "The high electrical conductivity of the region surrounding Earth, inferred from the observations of atmospheric whistlers and the zodiacal light, requires abandoning the customary models for producing geomagnetic (transient variations). . . . It becomes necessary to adopt a purely hydromagnetic approach wherein one focuses his attention only on the magnetic lines of force of the geomagnetic field and their displacement with the conducting gas surrounding Earth."

In this Chapter, a review of geomagnetism is presented, with special emphasis on those aspects of special interest to research and development in space, technology. Sections 8.2, 8.3, and 8.4 contain descriptions of the spherical harmonic analysis and other static magnetic-field parameters. Transient variations are discussed in Section 8.5.

8.2. MAIN GEOMAGNETIC FIELD

The geomagnetic field is quantitatively described in terms of magnetic elements that specify the strength and orientation of the field at the Earth's surface. There are several sets of elements which can be used for this purpose—the most commonly used ones are listed in Table 8-1.

TABLE 8-1

MAGNETIC ELEMENTS

Element	Description
F	Total magnetic intensity
I	Inclination or magnetic dip; defined as the smallest angle between the horizontal and the direction of the magnetic-field vector; positive in regions where the north-seeking end of a freely suspended magnetized needle points downward; thus magnetic dip is positive over most of the northern hemisphere
D	Magnetic variation or declination, defined as the angle between true north and the magnetic north indicated by a compass; positive when the magnetic north is to the east of true north
H	Intensity of the horizontal component of the geomagnetic field; always positive
V	Intensity of the vertical component of the geomagnetic field; has the same sign as I

Occasionally X, Y, and Z are used for the magnetic elements; X and Y are respectively the north and east components of H, and these directions define the positive values; *i.e.*, the south and west components are negative and Z is the same as V.

Figures 8-1 through **8-6** represent the best present knowledge of the main field over the surface of the Earth, taken from Hydrographic Office charts,

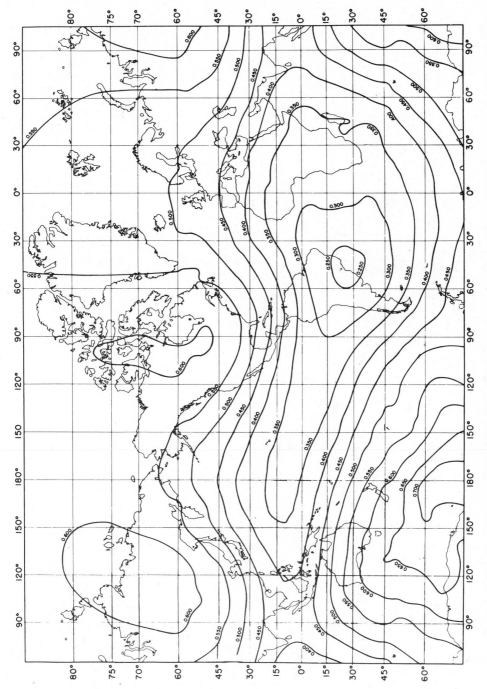

Fig. 8-1. Total intensity F of the Earth's magnetic field (in gauss). *Air Force Geophysics Research Directorate* (1960), *reproduced with permission of Macmillan Co.*

121

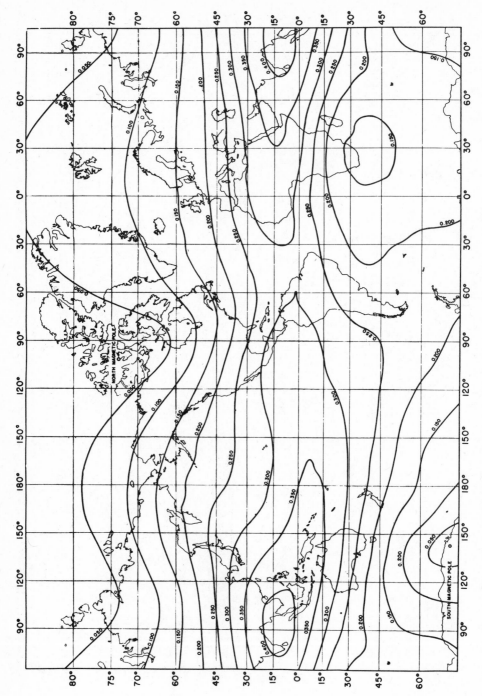

FIG. 8-2. Horizontal intensity H of the Earth's magnetic field (in gauss). *Air Force Geophysics Research Directorate* (1960), *reproduced with permission of Macmillan Co.*

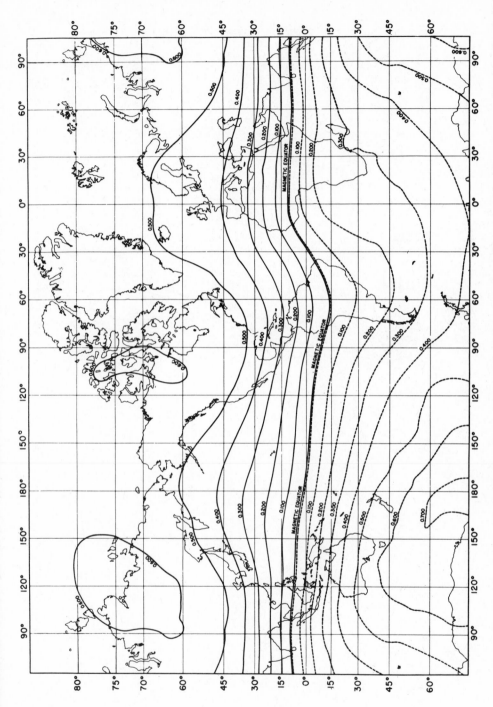

FIG. 8-3. Vertical intensity Z of the Earth's magnetic field (in gauss). Full lines designate the vertical intensity over areas of positive dip; dashed lines, areas of negative dip. *Air Force Geophysics Research Directorate (1960), reproduced with permission of Macmillan Co.*

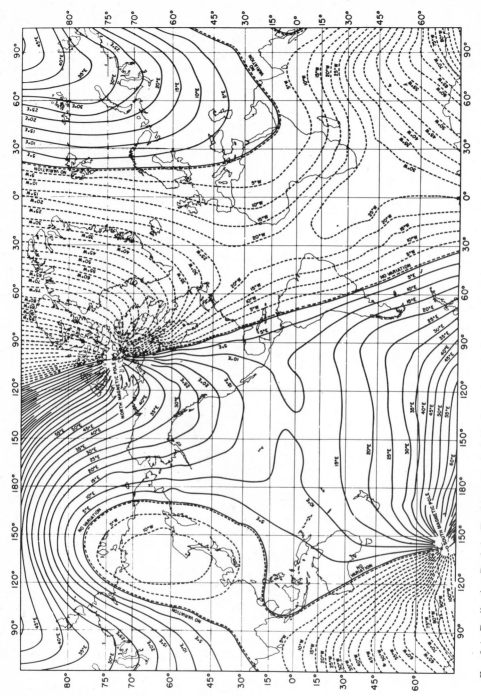

FIG. 8-4. Declination D of the Earth's magnetic field. Isogonic lines denote the variation or magnetic declination in degrees; full lines designate easterly (positive) variation, dashed lines westerly (negative) variation. *Air Force Geophysics Research Directorate (1960), reproduced with permission of Macmillan Co.*

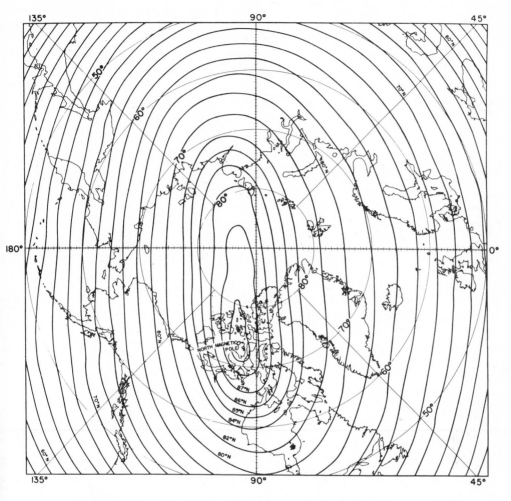

Fig. 8-5. Inclination or dip I of the Earth's magnetic field for the north-polar area. Isoclinic lines denote magnetic inclination or dip in degrees. *Air Force Geophysics Research Directorate (1960), reproduced with permission of Macmillan Co.*

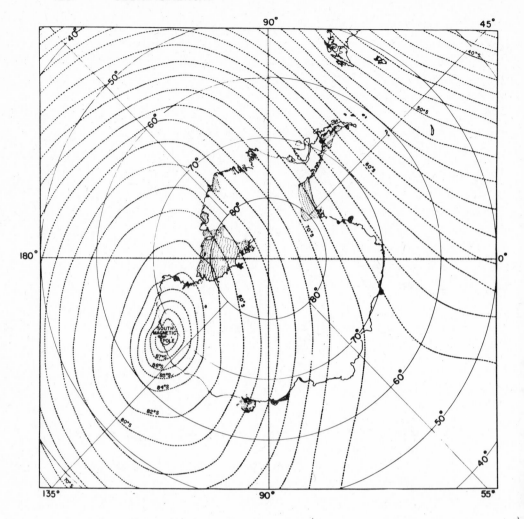

Fig. 8-6. Inclination or dip I of the Earth's magnetic field for the south-polar area. Isoclinic lines denote magnetic inclination or dip in degrees. *Air Force Geophysics Research Directorate (1960), reproduced with permission of Macmillan Co.*

which are published every five years (Air Force Geophysics Research Directorate, 1960). The total intensity F, the horizontal intensity H, the vertical intensity Z, the declination D, and the inclination I for both polar regions are shown. The secular change, which amounts to about one-tenth of one per cent per year of the total field, can be found on charts prepared by the Hydrographic Office in the 1700 series. The accuracy of the main field charts reproduced in this report depends on how well the various parts of the Earth are surveyed magnetically. In the United States, the charts are probably accurate within 0.1 per cent, but at high latitudes and in other less accessible areas, the errors are considerably larger. Surface anomalies on the order of 1000 miles or less in extent do not appear on the charts. In some places, these local anomalies may constitute an important fraction of the total field.

8.3.   SPHERICAL HARMONIC ANALYSIS OF MAIN FIELD

The first spherical harmonic analysis of the main geomagnetic field at the Earth's surface was made by Gauss in the nineteenth century. A number of authors, using improved data and varying numbers of coefficients, have performed harmonic analyses since then. The early works have been discussed by Chapman and Bartels (1940) ; more recent work has been done by Vestine *et al.* (1947), Finch and Leaton (1957), and Fanselau and Kautzleben (1958).

Assuming an internal origin for the geomagnetic field, we can derive the field from a potential of the form

$$V = a \sum_{n=1}^{\infty} \sum_{n=0}^{n} (a/r)^{n+1} \left(g_n{}^m \cos m\phi + h_n{}^m \sin m\phi \right) P_n{}^m (\cos \theta) , \quad (8\text{-}1)$$

where, in a right-handed system of geocentric·spherical coordinates,

a is the radius of the Earth,
r is the distance to the field point from the Earth's center,
θ is the geographic co-latitude (*i.e.*, polar angle),
ϕ is the east longitude,
$P_n{}^m (\cos \theta)$ is the normalized associated Legendre polynomial of degree n and order m, and
$g_n{}^m$ and $h_n{}^m$ are the gaussian coefficients determined from the surface magnetic data.

The gradients of the potential function give the magnetic-field components that are observed at the Earth's surface ($r = a$) ; *i.e.*,

$$X = \frac{1}{r} \frac{\partial V}{\partial \theta} , \quad Y = -\frac{1}{r \sin \theta} \frac{\partial V}{\partial \phi} , \quad Z = \frac{\partial V}{\partial r} . \qquad (8\text{-}2)$$

A recent harmonic analysis of the main field has been performed by Fanselau and Kautzleben (1958). The gaussian coefficients, which have the same physical dimensions as the magnetic-field intensity, are presented in Table 8-2. The

TABLE 8-2

Gaussian Coefficients g_n^m and h_n^m to $m = n = 15$, Epoch 1945.0

g_n^m $(10^{-4}$ gauss)

m/n	1	2	3	4	5	6	7	8	9	10	11	12	13	14	15
0	-3066.78	-127.89	+111.91	+91.02	-26.92	+4.35	+8.99	-0.28	+2.41	-1.34	+0.38	-0.31	+0.13	-0.94	+0.80
1	-216.03	+295.96	-174.54	+77.44	+30.31	+10.57	-7.44	+3.46	-0.50	+1.12	-1.73	+1.06	-0.56	-0.67	+1.96
2		+154.70	+124.27	+53.56	+20.83	-3.15	+5.60	-7.44	+5.62	-5.13	+2.50	-1.39	+0.44	+0.00	-0.78
3			+89.89	-38.79	-4.56	-26.77	+3.04	-1.74	-1.09	-1.40	+1.18	+0.23	-0.61	-0.03	-0.69
4				+36.20	-16.41	-0.02	-4.33	+2.70	-0.42	+2.19	-0.53	+0.93	+0.32	+0.56	-0.14
5					-7.88	+3.50	-2.05	+1.31	+0.99	+0.78	+0.43	-0.10	+0.56	+0.61	-0.34
6						-11.44	+2.62	-1.62	-1.04	+0.86	-0.01	-0.01	-0.27	-0.31	-0.78
7							+2.03	+1.03	-0.47	-0.47	-0.11	-0.34	-0.77	+0.03	+0.20
8								+1.01	+0.04	-0.71	+0.12	-0.81	+0.36	-0.10	+0.14
9									+1.67	-0.38	-0.04	-0.38	+0.25	+0.45	-0.73
10										+0.06	-0.44	+0.73	-0.64	+0.34	+0.05
11											+2.15	-0.79	+0.54	-0.10	-0.29
12												-0.05	+0.64	+0.33	+0.04
13													-0.76	+0.47	+0.02
14														-0.27	-0.53
15															+0.08

h_n^m $(10^{-4}$ gauss)

m/n	1	2	3	4	5	6	7	8	9	10	11	12	13	14	15
1	+577.35	-167.29	-53.40	+13.03	+3.60	-6.44	+2.02	-3.91	+1.82	-0.84	+0.86	-2.39	+1.41	-0.24	+0.48
2		+58.11	+16.63	-25.21	+8.36	+15.40	-1.85	+1.45	+0.08	+1.57	-1.05	+2.05	-0.64	+0.35	+1.16
3			+8.50	-9.52	+0.70	-2.05	+2.33	+1.48	-0.54	+2.39	-1.00	+2.45	-0.50	+1.26	-0.36
4				-12.85	-13.49	+0.25	+0.07	-1.22	+0.62	-0.44	+0.24	+0.22	+0.48	-0.47	+0.38
5					+12.58	-1.07	+4.09	+0.85	+1.68	-0.72	+0.93	-0.81	+0.47	-0.43	-0.20
6						-2.35	-1.03	+1.70	+1.03	+0.37	+0.09	-0.33	+0.40	+0.07	+0.70
7							-2.58	+0.13	+1.50	-0.61	-0.18	-0.07	+0.24	-0.29	+0.08
8								-1.04	-0.37	+0.52	-0.98	-0.18	+0.21	-0.12	-0.47
9									-0.34	+0.06	+0.43	+0.32	+0.44	-0.39	-0.30
10										+0.72	-0.54	-0.04	-0.67	-0.46	-0.80
11											-0.52	-0.37	-0.15	-0.46	-0.67
12												-0.48	-1.03	-0.03	-0.50
13													+0.51	-0.80	+0.38
14														-0.85	+0.16
15															+0.95

field described by these coefficients represents the gross features of the observed surface field to within about 1 per cent.

Equations for deriving the position of a single centered or eccentric dipole which represents a reasonable approximation to the geomagnetic field have been given by Bartels (1936). A first approximation to the Earth's magnetic field corresponds to a magnetic dipole situated at the geographic center of the Earth and inclined at an angle of 11° to the geographic axis. The axis of the centered dipole intersects the surface of the Earth and defines the geomagnetic poles. Hence, it also defines the geomagnetic coordinate system. **Figure 8-7** shows the geomagnetic coordinate system superimposed on a Mercator projection in geographic coordinates according to Vestine *et al.* (1948). The geomagnetic poles are not the same as the magnetic poles that are indicated on magnetic-field maps. The magnetic poles shown on maps are the dip poles, which are the points on the Earth's surface where the magnetic field is vertical. Thus the magnetic poles shown in **Fig. 8-5** and **8-6** are dip poles and are not coincident with the geomagnetic poles, which are derived from the centered-dipole approximation.

An improved approximation to the observed geomagnetic field is provided by a dipole located at the magnetic center of the Earth (the eccentric dipole). The position of the eccentric dipole has been determined by Parkinson and Cleary (1958) from the harmonic analysis of Finch and Leaton (1957). The location and orientation of the eccentric dipole for the epoch 1955.0 is given in the following quotation from Parkinson and Cleary (1958):

> "The eccentric dipole is displaced by 0.0685 Earth radii (about 436 km) from the center towards a point at latitude 15.6° N, longitude 150.9° E (just east of the Marianas). This is 6.6°, or 730 km north of the geomagnetic equator. The poles of the eccentric dipole (*i.e.*, the points where its axis cuts the surface of the Earth) are at 81.0° N, 84.7° W and at 75.0° S, 120.4° E (*i.e.*, in Ellesmere Is. and in Wilkes Land). The axis of the eccentric dipole is not vertical at these points, but is inclined at 3.9° to the vertical in the direction of the corresponding geomagnetic pole. . . . The field of the eccentric dipole is, of course, parallel to its axis, and so it also is inclined to the vertical at the poles of the eccentric dipole. The eccentric dipole field is vertical at two points which are further from the geomagnetic poles. The positions of these points are 82.4° N, 137.3° W and 67.9° S, 130.6° E. . . ."

The approximate geographic locations of the various magnetic poles are summarized in Table 8-3.

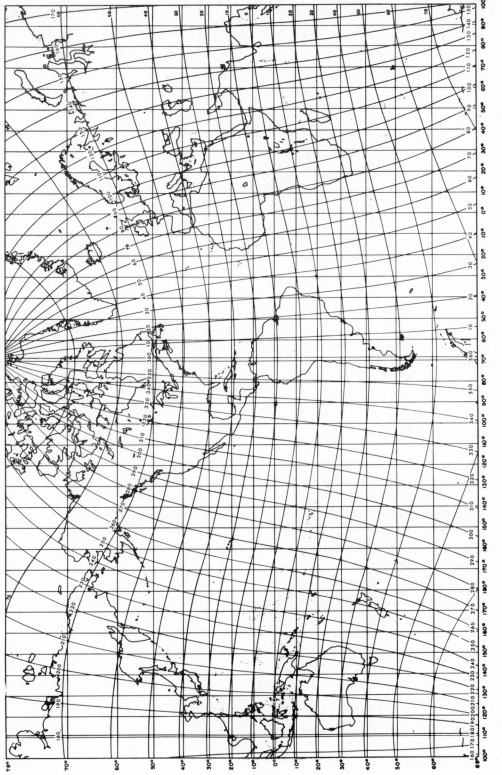

FIG. 8-7. Geomagnetic dipole field coordinate grid (curved lines) superimposed on a Mercator projection of the world.

TABLE 8-3

GEOGRAPHIC LATITUDE AND LONGITUDE OF THE MAGNETIC DIP POLES

As defined by	Northern Hemisphere	Southern Hemisphere
Observed Field	74° N, 259° E	68° S, 144° E
Centered Dipole (Geomagnetic Poles)	79° N, 291° E	79° S, 111° E
Eccentric Dipole	82° N, 223° E	68° S, 131° E

The geomagnetic coordinate system (based on the centered-dipole approximation) has only limited usefulness in analyzing phenomena that are geomagnetically controlled, *e.g.,* aurora and the geographical distribution of the Van Allen radiation. The centered-dipole model is a crude, first-order approximation to the geomagnetic field; hence, it is not surprising to find errors of several degrees in the predicted location of geomagnetically related regions.

A more useful magnetic parameter is the magnetic or dip latitude, which can be obtained from the relationship between latitude and dip angle for a perfect dipole,

$$\lambda_m = \arctan \left[\tfrac{1}{2} \tan I \right] ,$$

where λ_m is the magnetic or dip latitude, and I is the observed magnetic inclination or dip. When applied to the Earth's magnetic field, this formula is empirically found to give a better fit than geomagnetic coordinates to the geographic distribution of geomagnetically controlled phenomena.

An even better description of the geomagnetic field and one more physically meaningful is given by the integral invariant, described in Section 3.2.1. By means of the integral invariant, the path or trace of the mirror point of a particle trapped in the geomagnetic field can be described analytically. **Figure 8-8** outlines a coordinate system based on the calculations of Jensen *et al.* (1960). Trace 0 is the integral-invariant equator. The altitude to a fixed magnetic-field value is given in kilometers along each integral-invariant trace for the case where the magnetic-field value was arbitrarily chosen to be that near 1500 km at 120° E longitude. The altitudes elsewhere are then defined by the integral invariant. This figure shows very nicely the displacement of the eccentric dipole derived by Parkinson and Cleary.

8.4. MAIN FIELD ABOVE THE EARTH

Vestine *et al.* (1947) indicate that at least 99 per cent of the main magnetic field at the surface of the Earth originates from sources within the Earth. When the magnetic field is known at all points on a closed surface that encompasses

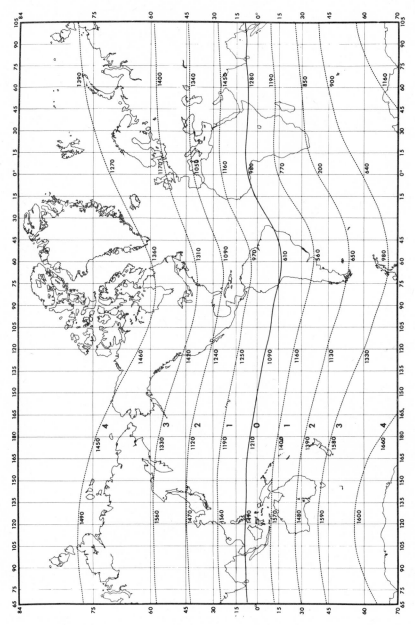

Fig. 8-8. Integral-invariant traces superimposed on a Mercator projection of the world. Trace 0 is the integral-invariant equator and may be considered the best approximation to the magnetic equator. Altitudes (in kilometers) to arbitrarily selected field values of 0.20, 0.22, 0.28, 0.30, and 0.32 gauss are given at 60° intervals along magnetically conjugate pairs of traces 0, 1, 2, 3, and 4, respectively. These altitudes show the displacement of the Earth's magnetic center from the geographic center.

the sources of the field, the field is completely determined at all points outside the surface. The potential of the main field given in Eq. (8-1) may be expressed in the form

$$V = \sum_{n=1}^{\infty} \frac{a^{n+2}}{r^{n+1}} T_n ,$$ (8-3)

where

$$T_n = \sum_{m=0}^{n} (g_n{}^m \cos m\phi + h_n{}^m \sin m\phi) P_n{}^m (\cos \theta) .$$ (8-4)

The field at the surface $r = a$ is determined by $g_n{}^m$ and $h_n{}^m$. In order to compute the field at an altitude h above the Earth, let $a_1 = a + h$; then V may be written in the convenient form

$$V = \sum_{n=1}^{\infty} \frac{a_1{}^{n+2}}{r^{n+1}} T_n \left(\frac{a}{a_1} \right)^{n+2} .$$ (8-5)

It is seen that the gauss coefficients of degree n are diminished in the ratio $(a/a_1)^{n+2}$ at altitude h. Local anomalies which correspond to harmonics of much higher degree are thus reduced effectively with elevation. The intensity of the dipole field and its components decreases outward as the cube of the distance from the center of the Earth. The contributions to the geomagnetic field of harmonic terms of $n = 2, 3, 4, 5$, and so on decrease outward proportional to r^{-4}, r^{-5}, r^{-6}, and r^{-7}, respectively. Consequently, the greater the distance from the Earth, the more dipolar is the permanent field; contributions to field variations by sheet currents or ring currents are excluded from consideration for the present. It may be anticipated that the fit between the observed and the computed values of the permanent field will be better at altitude h than at the Earth's surface, since a limited number of terms cannot represent accurately the fine detail of the anomalies in the surface field.

The 48-term harmonic analysis of the geomagnetic field has been used by Vestine and Sibley (private communication) to calculate the field distribution around the Earth. Some of the results of these calculations are shown in **Fig. 8-9, 8-10**, and **8-11**, where the altitudes of constant field strengths 0.100 and 0.010 gauss and the total field strength at 5000-km altitude are shown.

For various geophysical applications, it is of value to know the path of the lines of force of the geomagnetic field. Vestine and Sibley (1960) have computed the intersection with the Earth's surface of lines of force between the southern hemisphere and the northern hemisphere, based on the first 48 gauss coefficients. **Figure 8-12** represents the results of their calculations.

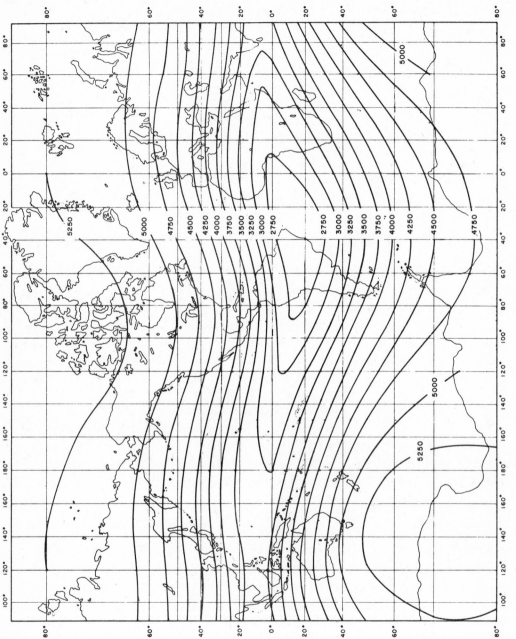

Fig. 8-9. Altitudes (in kilometers) to the surface of constant total field $F = 0.10$ gauss.

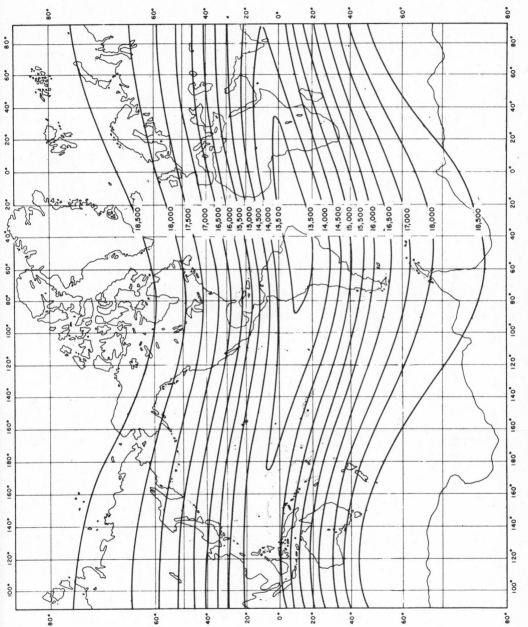

Fig. 8-10. Altitudes (in kilometers) to the surface of constant total field $F = 0.01$ gauss.

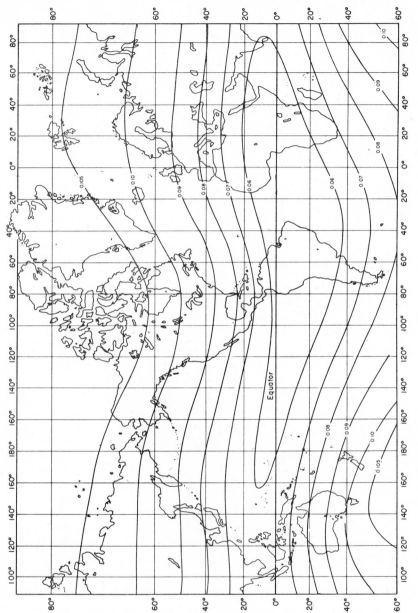

FIG. 8-11. Contours of total field strength F (in gauss) at 5000-km altitude.

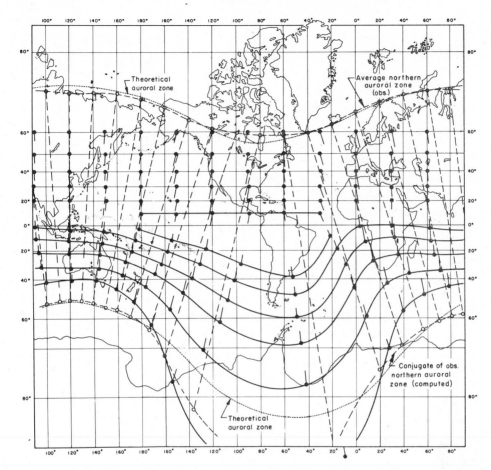

FIG. 8-12. Approximate intersections of lines of force of the geomagnetic field with the Earth's surface in the northern and southern hemispheres, based on the first 48 gauss coefficients. The points of intersection are shown by dots, associated in pairs; the short lines extending from the dots indicate the direction to the associated point. The association of points in the northern and southern auroral zones is also shown, but here the pairs are joined by dashed lines. *Vestine and Sibley (1960), reproduced with permission of J. Geophys. Research.*

8.5. VARIATIONS IN THE GEOMAGNETIC FIELD

The direction and magnitude of the Earth's magnetic field are constantly fluctuating, and these variations are recorded continuously at magnetic observatories distributed over the Earth. The variations in the Earth's magnetic field may be separated into two types: (1) secular variations, which are very slow, requiring hundreds of years to produce a change of a few per cent; and (2) transient variations, which disturb the field for periods ranging from a fraction of a second to a few years.

The secular variation is due to changes in the current system within the Earth's core. These changes usually amount to less than 0.1 per cent per year of the geomagnetic field over most of the Earth's surface. At any given location, the secular change is not a constant; rather, it changes in magnitude and occasionally in sign from year to year in such a way that hundreds or even thousands of years are required to produce, for example, a 1 per cent change in the Earth's magnetic moment.

A useful measure of the transient geomagnetic activity recorded by observatory magnetometers is available in the form of the "3-hourly range index" or K index—a figure indicating the magnetic character over a given 3-hr period. The K-index scale is defined for each observatory in terms of the amplitude of the magnetic variations during each 3-hr period. This index varies from 0 to 9, with $K = 0$ indicating magnetic quiet or calm, while $K = 9$ signifies great fluctuations in the geomagnetic field. The K indexes from the individual observatories are combined into a world-wide or planetary index—the K_p index—which is published periodically in a convenient form in the *Journal of Geophysical Research*.

The transient variations in the geomagnetic field arise from changing electric currents flowing in the ionized regions of the atmosphere and/or from hydromagnetic waves generated by interactions between solar plasma and the geomagnetic field. Most of the transient variations are due to interactions between the geomagnetic field and ionized gas moving out from the sun. This gas, which is thought to flow radially outward, is referred to as the solar wind (Parker, 1958). The best direct evidence for the existence of a continuous solar wind comes from the comet-tail observations of Biermann (1953). The solar wind will push into the geomagnetic field roughly to the point where the kinetic-energy density of the solar wind is equal to the magnetic-field-energy density. By equating these two energy densities and assuming that the magnetic field strength is given by

$$B = B_0 \, (R_e/r)^3 \, ,$$

where B_0 is the field strength at the Earth's surface, R_e is the radius of the Earth or 6.37×10^8 cm, and r is the radial distance to the point where the field strength is B, we obtain

$$r \approx R_e \left[\frac{B_0{}^2}{4 \pi n m v^2} \right]^{1/6} . \tag{8-6}$$

In cgs units, n is the number of solar-wind protons per cubic centimeter, m is their average mass in grams, and v is the solar-wind velocity in centimeters per second. Taking $B_0 = 0.35$ gauss, $n = 30$ protons (and electrons)/cm³, and $v = 3 \times 10^7$ cm/sec for moderate solar activity, we find that the solar wind will penetrate to $r = 7.7\ R_e$. These values for the solar-wind parameters are based on recent work of Biermann (private communication). The solar wind blowing against the geomagnetic field will probably distort the field into the shape shown in **Fig. 8-13** (Johnson, 1960a). The front surface is determined by the impact pressure of the solar wind while the long "tail" is closed by the pressure of the transverse thermal motion of the solar-wind particles. In all cases, the plasma pressure is equal to $B^2/(8\pi)$ at the interface.

The interface between the solar wind and the geomagnetic field is unstable (Dungey, 1955; Parker, 1958) in a manner somewhat analogous to the classical hydrodynamic Helmholtz instability (*e.g.,* a flag fluttering in the wind or wind-generated water waves). These instabilities take the form of hydromagnetic waves that propagate through the geomagnetic field and that are observed at the Earth's surface as small fluctuations in the geomagnetic field. Hydromagnetic waves are also generated by changes in pressure on the geomagnetic-field boundary when the density or velocity of the solar wind varies. A discussion of some of the more important features of hydromagnetic-wave propagation through the geomagnetic field is given in Section 8.6.

Other observed transient variations are: auroral-type fluctuations (Campbell, 1960); micropulsations and other extra-low-frequency (ELF) phenomena, the cause of which, at present, is not understood (Benioff, 1960); diurnal variations, caused by tidal motions induced in the ionosphere by solar heating; seasonal variations, possibly due to changes in the conductivity of the ionosphere as a function of solar angle; an 11-year variation (in phase with the solar cycle), which is due either to changes in the total particle energy stored in the geomagnetic field or to variations in the pressure of the solar wind incident on the geomagnetic field.

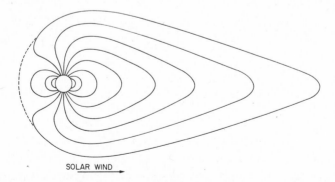

SOLAR WIND

Fɪɢ. 8-13. Probable distortion of the geomagnetic field by the solar wind on a magnetically disturbed day. The dashed line represents the position of the interface between the geomagnetic field and the solar wind. *Astronautics (April, 1960), reproduced with permission of American Rocket Society.*

The two most important transient variations are the diurnal variations and the fluctuations produced during geomagnetic storms by hydromagnetic waves. The diurnal variation is reasonably predictable for a given location and usually involves field changes of the order of 0.1 per cent of the total field. Except within a band near the integral-invariant equator, the diurnal variation is characterized by a minimum value for the field near local noon. Within the latitude range of about ±10 deg. of the integral-invariant equator, the sign of the variation is reversed, with the field showing an increase near local noon. The decrease at mid-latitude amounts to about $50\,\gamma$ $(1\,\gamma = 10^{-5}$ gauss), while the increase near the dip equator is approximately $100\,\gamma$ in amplitude.

Geomagnetic storms are disturbances which occur in the magnetic field with a frequency varying with the solar cycle. As described by Chapman and Bartels (1940), the average characteristics of geomagnetic storms are summarized in Table 8-4. Almost all magnetic storms display smoothed characteristics which fall within a factor of 3 of the numbers given in the table. A hydromagnetic model for geomagnetic storms (Dessler and Parker, 1959) provides an explanation of the causes of the observed phases; these causes are also summarized in Table 8-4.

8.6. HYDROMAGNETIC-WAVE PROPAGATION

Hydromagnetic waves are simply a form of electromagnetic wave appropriate to the medium in which they propagate. This fact is clear from the derivation in which hydromagnetic-wave propagation follows from Maxwell's equations (Alfvén, 1950, p. 84). Thus hydromagnetic waves are subject to the same laws of reflection, refraction, and absorption as any other electromagnetic wave, with some modifications imposed in certain cases by a particular mode of propagation (*e.g.,* Karplus, 1960).

For conditions applicable to the Earth's outer ionosphere, the hydromagnetic wave velocity is given by

$$V_{hm} = B/(4\,\pi\,\rho)^{1/2} ,$$

where ρ is the mass density of the ionized component in g/cm³. The velocity of hydromagnetic waves propagating in the magnetic equatorial plane versus altitude is shown in **Fig. 8-14** (Dessler *et al.,* 1960). For nonequatorial latitudes, the velocity shown should be multiplied by $(1 + 3\,\sin^2\,\lambda_m)^{1/2}$, where λ_m is the magnetic latitude. This curve applies for both longitudinal and transverse waves. The ion-density values given by Johnson (1960b) were adopted in calculating this curve.

The propagation time and ray paths for hydromagnetic waves have been studied quantitatively for a two-dimensional model by Dessler *et al.* (1960).

TABLE 8-4

Geomagnetic Storms

Features	Characteristics	Causes
Sudden Commencement	Horizontal component H of Earth's magnetic field increases in low and temperate latitudes; this increase, typically 20 to 30 γ, is largest at equatorial stations, with a rise time of 2 to 6 min.	Initiated by impact of solar plasma on geomagnetic field—sharp increase in strength of solar wind; effect of impact carried to lower ionosphere by hydromagnetic waves; sharp leading edge of solar plasma produced by weak magnetic field and plasma normally present in interplanetary space.
Initial Phase	H remains above normal undisturbed value (NUV) for 2 to 8 hr.	Increased solar-wind pressure on geomagnetic field; continues until solar-wind pressure relaxes.
Main Phase	H is farther below NUV than it was above NUV during Initial Phase; has decrease of 50 to 100 γ; after minimum is reached, H slowly recovers toward NUV, rate of recovery increasing with time—H-vs.-time curve is saucer shaped (d^2H/dt^2 is positive); phase lasts from 12 to 24 hr and tends to be noisy; large positive and negative excursions, with amplitudes of the order of several hundred gamma and periods of approximately $\frac{1}{3}$ hr, occur in magnetic field; these excursions are not shown in average magnetic-storm data.	Stresses set up by trapped protons in geomagnetic field; stress from both centrifugal force of trapped particles oscillating along lines of force through equatorial plane and from repulsion of magnetic moment of trapped particle by magnetic moment of Earth; large-amplitude fluctuations probably due to changes in solar-wind pressure and/or major instabilities in flow of solar wind past geomagnetic field.
Recovery Phase	Recovery is nearly exponential toward NUV (d^2H/dt^2 is negative); recovery time-constant between 1 and 3 days, although 10- to 20-day recovery time not uncommon; often no other magnetic disturbances occur during this phase.	Main-Phase stress relieved through transfer of energy of trapped protons to neutral hydrogen in geocorona by means of ion-atom charge-exchange process.

Fig. 8-14. Velocity of hydromagnetic waves in the geomagnetic equatorial plane for a surface field of 0.315 gauss. For other latitudes, the velocity shown should be multiplied by $(1 + 3 \sin^2 \lambda_m)^{1/2}$, where λ_m is the magnetic latitude. This curve applies for both longitudinal and transverse waves, *i.e.*, propagation both along the magnetic field and perpendicular to it. *Dessler et al. (1960), reproduced with permission of J. Geophys. Research.*

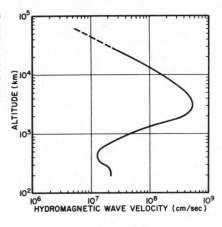

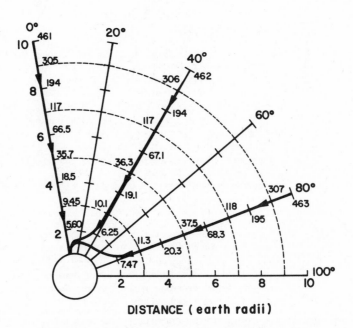

DISTANCE (earth radii)

Fig. 8-15. Three ray paths of hydromagnetic waves propagating in the geomagnetic equatorial plane to a point on the Earth from a distance of 10 Earth radii. The transit times in seconds for each ray to travel to the Earth are given at each Earth-radii distance. *Dessler et al. (1960), reproduced with permission of J. Geophys. Research.*

Three paths of hydromagnetic waves propagating (in the geomagnetic equatorial plane) to a point on the Earth from a distance of 10 Earth radii are shown in **Fig. 8-15**. The transit time for each ray to travel to the Earth is given at each Earth-radii distance.

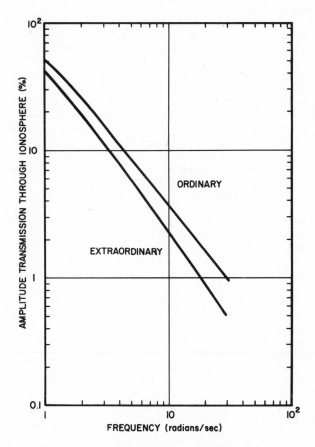

Fɪɢ. 8-16. Fractional amplitude transmission of hydromagnetic waves passing through the ionosphere versus incident angular frequency. These curves apply for daytime conditions near sunspot maximum. There is less attenuation at night and near sunspot minimum. *Francis and Karplus (1960), reproduced with permission of J. Geophys. Research.*

The attenuation and dissipation of energy of hydromagnetic waves passing through the ionosphere have been studied by Francis and Karplus (1960). The fraction of the incident-wave amplitude which passes through the ionosphere versus wave frequency is shown in **Fig. 8-16**.

REFERENCES

Air Force Geophysics Research Directorate, 1960, *Handbook of Geophysics,* Macmillan Co., New York, pp. 10-1 to 10-68.

Alfvén, H., 1950, *Cosmical Electrodynamics,* Oxford University Press, London.

Bartels, J., 1936, "The Eccentric Dipole Approximating the Earth's Magnetic Field," *Terr. Mag.* **41,** 225–250.

Benioff, Hugo, 1960, "Observations of Geomagnetic Fluctuations in the Period Range 0.3 to 120 Seconds," *J. Geophys. Research,* **65,** 1413–1422.

Biermann, L., 1953, "Physical Processes in Comet Tails and Their Relation to Solar Activity," *Mémoires de la Société Royale des Sciences de Liége,* Vol. 13, 291–302.

Campbell, W. H., 1960, "Magnetic Micropulsations and the Pulsating Aurora," *J. Geophys. Research,* **65,** 874.

Chapman, S., and J. Bartels, 1940, *Geomagnetism,* Oxford University Press, London.

Dessler, A. J., and E. N. Parker, 1959, "Hydromagnetic Theory of Geomagnetic Storms," *J. Geophys. Research,* **64,** 2239–2252.

Dessler, A. J., W. E. Francis, and E. N. Parker, 1960, "Geomagnetic Storm Sudden Commencement Rise Times, *J. Geophys. Research,* **65,** 2715–2719.

Dungey, J. W., 1955, "Electrodynamics of the Outer Atmosphere," *The Physics of the Ionosphere,* The Physical Society, London, pp. 229–236.

Elsasser, W. M., 1950, "The Earth's Interior and Geomagnetism," *Revs. Modern Phys.,* **22,** 1–35.

Fanselau, G., and H. Kautzleben, 1958, "Die Analytische Darstellung des Geomagnetischen Feldes," *Geofis. Pura e Applicata,* **41,** 33–72.

Finch, H. F., and B. R. Leaton, 1957, "The Earth's Main Magnetic Field—Epoch 1955," *Monthly Notices, Roy. Astron. Soc., Geophysical Supplements,* **7,** 314–317.

Francis, W. E., and Robert Karplus, 1960, "Hydromagnetic Waves in the Ionosphere," *J. Geophys. Research,* **65,** 3593–3600.

Jensen, D. C., R. W. Murray and J. A. Welch, Jr., 1960, "Tables of Adiabatic Invariants for the Geomagnetic Field 1955.0," Air Force Special Weapons Center, Kirtland Air Force Base, New Mexico.

Johnson, F. S., 1960a, "The Gross Character of the Geomagnetic Field in the Solar Wind," *J. Geophys. Research,* **65,** 3049–3051.

Johnson, F. S., 1960b, "The Ion Distribution Above the F_2 Maximum," *J. Geophys. Research,* **65,** 577–584.

Karplus, Robert, 1960, "Radiation of Hydromagnetic Waves," *Phys. Fluids,* **3,** 800–805.

Parker, E. N., 1956, "On the Geomagnetic Storm Effect," *J. Geophys. Res.,* **61,** 625–637.

Parker, E. N., 1958 ,"Interaction of the Solar Wind with the Geomagnetic Field," *Phys. Fluids,* **1,** 171–187.

Parkinson, W. D., and J. Cleary, 1958, "The Eccentric Geomagnetic Dipole," *Geophys. J.,* **1,** 346.

Vestine, E. H., L. Laporte, I. Lange, and W. E. Scott, 1947, "The Geomagnetic Field, Its Description and Analysis," Publication No. 580, Carnegie Institution of Washington, Washington, D.C.

Vestine, E. H., L. Laporte, I. Lange, C. Cooper, and W. C. Hendrix, 1948, "Description of the Earth's Main Magnetic Field and Its Secular Change 1905–1945," Publication No. 578, Carnegie Institution of Washington, Washington, D.C.

Vestine, E. H., and W. L. Sibley, 1960, "The Geomagnetic Field in Space, Ring Currents, and Auroral Isochasms," *J. Geophys. Research,* **65,** 1967–1979.

Appendix

Supplementary Data

SOLAR-SYSTEM DATA

Member of Solar System	Solar Distance				Orbit Inclination	Orbit Eccentricity	Mean Radius (km)	Mass (g)
	Mean (A.U.)	Mean (km)	Minimum (km)	Maximum (km)				
Mercury	0.387	5.79×10^7	4.59×10^7	6.97×10^7	7°00'	0.206	2.42×10^3	3.58×10^{26}
Venus	0.723	1.08×10^8	1.07×10^8	1.088×10^8	3°23'	0.007	6.16×10^3	4.90×10^{27}
Earth	1.000	1.49×10^8	1.458×10^8	1.520×10^8	0°00'	0.017	6.37×10^3	5.975×10^{27}
Mars	1.524	2.38×10^8	2.06×10^8	2.49×10^8	1°51'	0.093	3.33×10^3	6.58×10^{26}
Jupiter	5.203	7.78×10^8	6.39×10^8	8.14×10^8	1°18'	0.048	6.99×10^4	1.90×10^{29}
Saturn	9.539	1.426×10^9	1.344×10^9	1.502×10^9	2°29'	0.056	5.75×10^4	5.69×10^{28}
Moon	0.00258^a	3.84×10^{5a}	3.63×10^{5a}	4.04×10^{5a}	...	0.055	1.738×10^3	7.343×10^{25}
Sun	...	...	...	...	...	...	1.3914×10^6	1.987×10^{33}

Member of Solar System	Visual Albedo	Surface Temperature (°K)	Density (g/cm³)	Surface Gravity^d	Rotation Period	Sidereal Revolution Period (yr)	Mean Orbit Velocity (km/sec)	Escape Velocity (km/sec)
Mercury	0.058	690	6.2	0.30	88 d (?)	0.241	47.85	4.2
Venus	0.76	293 (?)	5.0	0.90	30 hr (?)	0.615	35.01	10.3
Earth	0.39	288	5.52	1.00	23.93 hr	1.000	29.76	11.2
Mars	0.148	235	3.81	0.38	24.6 hr	1.88	24.11	5.0
Jupiter	0.51	135	1.36	2.65	9.9 hr	11.86	13.05	61
Saturn	0.50	120	0.72	1.14	10.2 hr	29.46	9.64	37
Moon	0.072	120–400	3.3	0.17	27.3 d	0.075	1.03^c	2.4
Sun	...	5800	1.41	27.9	27 d^b	...	...	620

^{a} Distance from Earth.
^{b} 24.65 near equator, increasing with latitude to 30.9 d at 60° and about 34 d near the poles.
^{c} Velocity relative to Earth.
^{d} Gravity relative to Earth.

147

EARTH SATELLITES AND SPACE PROBES—APRIL 24, 1961

Designation	Name	Weight (kg)	Launch Date	Initial Altitude Perigee (km)	Initial Altitude Apogee (km)	Decay Date	Major Purpose
1957 Alpha 1	Sputnik I	3500	10-4-57	280	950	12-1-57	Sputnik I launcher
1957 Alpha 2	—	84	10-4-57	230	950	1-4-58	Earth orbit
1957 Beta	Sputnik II	3600	11-3-57	230	1670	4-14-58	Radiation measurement (contained dog, no recovery attempted)
1958 Alpha	Explorer I	14	1-31-58	370	2540	~1966	Cosmic-ray measurement (discovered Van Allen belt)
1958 Beta 1	—	23	3-17-58	660	3950	~2500	Vanguard I launcher
1958 Beta 2	Vanguard I	1.47	3-17-58	660	3950	~3000	Geodesy, atmospheric density
1958 Gamma	Explorer III	14	3-26-58	190	2810	6-28-58	Radiation-belt measurement
1958 Delta 1	—	...	3-17-58	660	3950	~2500	Sputnik III launcher
1958 Delta 2	Sputnik III	1327	5-15-58	240	1880	4-6-60	General geophysical measurement
1958 Epsilon	Explorer IV	17.4	7-26-58	260	2200	10-23-59	Radiation-belt measurement
	Pioneer I	38.3	10-11-58	...	180,000	10-12-58	Space probe (did not escape from Earth)
	Pioneer III	5.87	12-6-58	...	160,000	12-7-58	Radiation measurement (did not escape from Earth)
1958 Zeta	Score	3969	12-18-58	180	1480	1-21-59	Radio-relay tests (Eisenhower's voice message)
	Lunik I (Mechta)	1472	1-2-59	(0.98)^a	(1.29)^b	...	Lunar and space probe
1959 Alpha 1	Vanguard II	9.41	2-17-59	560	3320	~2150	Cloud-cover measurement
1959 Alpha 2	—	23	2-17-59	560	3320	~2100	Vanguard II launcher
1959 Beta	Discoverer I	590	2-28-59	160	970	3-5-59	System checkout
	Pioneer IV	6.08	3-3-59	(0.99)^a	(1.15)^b	...	Space probe
1959 Gamma	Discoverer II	730	4-13-59	230	350	4-26-59	Attempted capsule recovery
1959 Delta	Explorer VI	64.4	8-7-59	250	42,400	Uncertain	General geophysical measurement
1959 Epsilon 1	Discoverer V	771	8-13-59	220	720	9-28-59^c	Attempted capsule recovery
1959 Epsilon 2	—	88	8-13-59	220	720	Uncertain	Discoverer V capsule
1959 Zeta	Discoverer VI	771	8-19-59	220	860	10-20-59	Attempted capsule recovery
	Lunik II	389.4	9-12-59	...	...	9-13-59	Lunar probe (impact)
1959 Eta	Vanguard III	45	9-18-59	510	3750	~2060	Magnetometer
1959 Theta	Lunik III	278.5	10-3-59	40,000	470,000	4-20-60	Lunar probe (far-side photograph)
1959 Iota 1	Explorer VII	41.5	10-13-59	550	1130	~2000	General geophysical measurement
1959 Iota 2	—	26.8	10-13-59	550	1130	~1990	Explorer VII launcher
1959 Kappa	Discoverer VII	771	11-7-59	160	840	11-26-59	Attempted capsule recovery
1959 Lambda	Discoverer VIII	771	11-20-59	210	1670	3-8-60	Attempted capsule recovery
1960 Alpha	Pioneer V	42.9	3-11-60	(0.81)^a	(0.99)^b	...	Space probe (magnetic and radiation measurements)
1960 Beta 1	—	23	4-1-60	700	750	~2050	Tiros I launcher
1960 Beta 2	Tiros I	122	4-1-60	700	750	~2050	Cloud-cover measurement (photographs)
1960 Gamma 1	—	570	4-13-60	370	800	1962	Transit IB launcher
1960 Gamma 2	Transit IB	120	4-13-60	370	800	~1966	Navigation system
1960 Delta	Discoverer XI	771	4-15-60	130	340	4-26-60	Attempted capsule recovery

Designation	Name		Date				Remarks
1960 Epsilon 1	Sputnik IV	2500	5-15-60	300	370	1963	Attempted capsule recovery
1960 Epsilon 2		2100	5-15-60	300	370	7-17-60	Sputnik IV launcher
1960 Zeta 1	Midas II	2270	5-24-60	480	520	~1972	Rocket-launch detector
1960 Eta 1	Transit IIA	101.1	6-22-60	620	1060	~2050	Navigation system
1960 Eta 2	Greb	19	6-22-60	620	1060	~2050	Solar radiation (piggy-back satellite)
1960 Eta 3		...	6-22-60	620	1060	~2050	Launcher
1960 Theta	Discoverer XIII	771	8-10-60	260	700	11-14-60	Capsule recovery
1960 Iota 1	Echo I	68	8-12-60	1400	1800	~1965	Global-communication test
1960 Iota 2		...	8-12-60	1400	1800	~6000	Echo I launcher
1960 Kappa	Discoverer XIV	771	8-18-60	190	810	9-16-60	Capsule recovery (capsule recovered in air)
1960 Lambda 1	Sputnik V	4590	8-19-60	300	340	8-20-60	Capsule recovery (contained dogs)
1960 Lambda 2		...	8-19-60	300	340	9-23-60	Sputnik V launcher
1960 Mu	Discoverer XV	771	9-13-60	200	610	10-18-60	Capsule recovery
1960 Nu 1	Courier IB	227	10-4-60	970	1240	~2250	Communication system
1960 Nu 2		...	10-4-60	970	1240	2250	Courier IB launcher
1960 Xi 1	Explorer VIII	40.89	11-3-60	490	2290	~2000	Radio-wave measurement
1960 Xi 2		26.8	11-3-60	490	2290	2000	Explorer VIII launcher
1960 Omicron	Discoverer XVII	771	11-12-60	180	990	12-29-60	Capsule recovery (capsule recovered in air)
1960 Pi 1	Tiros II	127	11-23-60	640	710	~2250	Cloud-cover measurement
1960 Pi 2		...	11-23-60	640	710	2250	Tiros II launcher
1960 Rho 1	Sputnik VI	4563	12-1-60	180	250	12-2-60	Capsule recovery
1960 Rho 2		...	12-1-60	180	250	12-2-60	Sputnik VI launcher
1960 Sigma	Discoverer XVIII	771	12-7-60	280	740	4-2-61	Capsule recovery (capsule recovered in air)
1960 Tau	Discoverer XIX	771	12-20-60	210	650	1-23-61	Infrared-radiation measurement
1961 Alpha 1	Samos II	1860	1-31-61	480	560	...	System check-out
1961 Beta 1	Sputnik VII	7214	2-4-61	220	380	2-26-61	General geophysical measurement
1961 Gamma 1	(Venus probe)	642	2-12-61	(0.72)[a]	(1.02)[b]	...	Space probe
1961 Gamma 3	Sputnik VIII	7214	2-12-61	240	480	2-25-61	Launch base for Gamma 1
1961 Delta 1	Explorer IX	6.6	2-16-61	640	2580	...	Drag measurement (Scout booster)
1961 Epsilon	Discoverer XX	1111	2-17-61	320	640	...	Capsule recovery
1961 Zeta	Discoverer XXI	1111	2-18-61	260	1080	...	Engine-restart test
1961 Eta 1	Transit IIIB	113	2-22-61	190	990	3-30-61	Navigation system
1961 Eta 2	Lofti	24.5	2-22-61	190	990	3-30-61	Radio-wave measurement (piggy-back satellite; did not separate from Transit IIIB)
1961 Theta 1	Sputnik IX	4700.9	3-9-61	240	250	3-9-61	Capsule recovery (dog recovered)
1961 Iota 1	Sputnik X	4695	3-25-61	179	248	3-25-61	Capsule recovery (dog recovered)
1961 Kappa	Explorer X	35.4	3-25-61	177	181,000	...	Magnetic-field and solar-wind measurement
1961 Lambda 1	DiscovererXXIII	1111	4-8-61	299	647	...	Capsule recovery
1961 Mu 1	Vostok	4715	4-12-61	175	302	4-12-61	First man in space (man recovered)
1961 Mu 2	...		4-12-61	175	302	4-16-61	Vostok launcher

[a] Perihelion in astronomical units (1.49×10^8 km).
[b] Aphelion in astronomical units.

CONVERSION FACTORS

Energy

1 ev = 1.6020×10^{-12} erg
1 joule = 10^7 ergs
1 hp-hr = 2.684×10^{13} ergs
1 kw-hr = 3.60×10^{13} ergs
1 ft-lb^a = 1.3558×10^7 ergs
1 ft-poundal = 4.344×10^5 ergs
1 Btu = 1.0549×10^{10} ergs
1 calorie = 4.184×10^7 ergs
Wavelength associated with 1 ev, 12395 A
Frequency associated with 1 ev, 2.4186×10^{14} cps
Wave number associated with 1 ev, 8067.8
Temperature corresponding to 1 ev, 11606° K

Power

1 hp = 745.65w = 7.4565×10^9 ergs/sec
1 ft-lb^a/sec = 1.3558 w = 1.3558×10^7 ergs/sec
1 w = 10^7 ergs/sec
1 Btu/sec = 1.0549×10^3 w = 1.0549×10^{10} ergs/sec
1 µw = 10^6 w = 10 ergs/sec

Mass

1 lb = 0.4536 kg = 453.6 g
1 slug = 32.174 lb = 1.4594×10^4 g

Pressure

1 psi^a = 70.31 g^a/cm^2 = 6.894×10^4 dyne/cm^2 = 51.71 mm Hg
1 lb^a/ft^2 = 0.4882 g^a/cm^2 = 4.788×10^2 dyne/cm^2 = 0.3591 mm Hg
1 g^a/cm^2 = 980.6 dyne/cm^2 = 0.7355 mm Hg
1 dyne/cm^2 = 7.502×10^{-4} mm Hg

Force

1 poundal = 1.3825×10^4 dynes
1 pound-force^a = 4.4481×10^5 dynes
1 newton = 10^5 dynes

Length

1 in. = 2.5400 cm
1 ft = 30.480 cm
1 yd = 91.440 cm
1 mile = 1.60935 km
1 nautical mile = 1.8532 km
1 µ = 10^{-4} cm
1 A = 10^{-8} cm

Temperature

To obtain °K from °C, add 273.16
To obtain °F from °C, multiply by 9/5 and add 32
To obtain °R from °K, multiply by 9/5

Electrical Units

1 coulomb = 2.998×10^9 statcoulomb = 0.1 abcoulomb
1 ampere = 2.998×10^9 statampere = 0.1 abampere
1 volt = 3.336×10^{-3} statvolt = 10^8 abvolt
1 ohm = 1.113×10^{-12} statohm = 10^9 abohm
1 farad = 8.988×10^{11} cm = 10^{-9} abfarad
1 henry = 1.113×10^{-12} stathenry = 10^9 cm
10^4 gauss = 1 weber/m^2

---

^{a} lb and g here are regarded as units of force, and the magnitudes of the forces are those exerted on unit masses by the Earth's sea-level gravitational field at 45° latitude.

USEFUL PHYSICAL CONSTANTS

Proton mass	1.6724×10^{-24} g
Electron mass	9.1058×10^{-28} g
Electronic charge	4.8028×10^{-10} esu
Rest-mass energy of proton	938.21 Mev
Rest-mass energy of electron	0.51098 Mev
Cyclotron frequency of proton in 1-gauss field	1.525×10^{3} cps
Cyclotron frequency of electron in 1-gauss field	2.80×10^{6} cps
Velocity of 1-ev proton	1.385×10^{6} cm/sec
Velocity of 1-ev electron	5.931×10^{7} cm/sec
Avogadro number	6.0248×10^{23} particles/mole
Loschmidt number	2.6872×10^{19} particles/cm^3
Boltzmann constant (k)	1.3804×10^{-16} erg/deg
Planck constant (h)	6.625×10^{-27} erg/sec
Stefan-Boltzmann constant (σ)	5.6724×10^{-5} erg/cm^2-deg^4-sec
Wien displacement-law constant	2.8979×10^{-1} cm deg
Velocity of light (c)	2.9979×10^{10} cm/sec
Mechanical equivalent of heat	4.184 joules/cal
Constant of gravitation (G)	6.670×10^{-8} dyne cm^2/g^2
Molar volume at STP	22.42×10^{3} cm^3/mole
Gas constant per mole (R_0)	8.317×10^{7} erg/mole-deg
Solar constant	0.140 watt/cm^2 ($= 2.00$ cal/cm^2-min)
Solar illuminance constant	13.67 lumens/cm^2
Visual magnitude of sun	-26.88
Standard atmospheric pressure	1.01325×10^{6} dyne/cm^2 (760 mm Hg)
Total mass of earth's atmosphere	5.14×10^{21} g
Density of air at STP	1.293×10^{-3} g/cm^3
Density of O_2 at STP	1.429×10^{-3} g/cm^3
Density of N_2 at STP	1.251×10^{-3} g/cm^3
Molecular weight of dry air	28.966
Specific heat of dry air at constant pressure (C_p)	0.240 cal/g-°K
constant volume (C_v)	0.171 cal/g-°K
Mean free path in air at STP	6.4×10^{-6} cm
Magnetic moment of Earth	8×10^{15} erg/gauss
Permeability of empty space (μ_0)	$4\pi \times 10^{-7}$ henry/m ($= 1.257 \times 10^{-6}$)
Permittivity of empty space (ε_0)	$10^{-9}/36\,\pi$ farad/m ($= 8.85 \times 10^{-12}$)
Velocity at which kinetic energy equals rest-mass energy	0.917 c
Acceleration of gravity at latitude λ	$978.05\,(1 + 0.00529\,\sin^2 \lambda)$ cm/sec^2 $= 980.6$ cm/sec^2 at $\lambda = 45°$

Index